WINDMILLS OF NORTHAMPTONSHIRE
and the Soke of Peterborough

WINDMILLS OF NORTHAMPTONSHIRE
and the Soke of Peterborough
A History of Twentieth Century Sites

To Gwendoline

best wishes

Trevor L. Stainwright

T. Stainwright

W. D. WHARTON
Wellingborough

First published in 1991 by
W.D. Wharton
37 Sheep Street
Wellingborough
Northamptonshire NN8 1BX

Trevor L. Stainwright asserts the moral right
to be identified as the author of this work

This book is dedicated to
the most important people in my life:
my wife Valerie and our daughter Katie

ISBN 0 9518557 0 0

Designed and typeset by John Hardaker, Wollaston, Northamptonshire
Printed and bound in Great Britain by The Bath Press, Bath

Contents

Acknowledgements

In the ten years it has taken me to write this book I have been lucky enough to meet with many fine people who have encouraged me to continue and improve my work. Local historians, owners and descendants of millers have supplied information and have allowed to be reproduced the precious and rare photographs that appear in this book. I thank the following:

Mr Kenneth I. Woolley, Mr Phil Kingston, Mr Charles Burbridge, the late Miss Mabel Little, Mr R. T. Walker, Mr A. R. Lane, Mr Leslie W. Herne, Mrs Mary Furniss, and Mrs Janet Blake, who makes lovely coffee.

Others subjected to my constant questioning include Miss Florence C. A. Colyer, Mr Phillip Davis, the late Mrs Clifton, Mr Clive R. Hawkes, Mr and Mrs R. W. Campbell, Mr T. Gater, The Reverend Canon P. J. M. Bryan MA, Mr Frank Coles and Mrs Alice Thomas to whom I am especially grateful for inviting me to dinner.

Past memories were supplied by Mr M. D. Wilford, the late Mrs Dickens, the late Russell Key, Miss Margaret Holdich, Mr William Dilley and the late Arthur Claypole. Thanks also to Mr Ron Claypole, Father Geoffrey Ward, Mr Sidney Spademan, Mr W. P. Gosset, Mr F. A. Moore, the Reverend A. J. Francis, Mr R. M. Warwick, Mr Cyril Putt, Mr Roy Pentelow, Mr Brian Hensman, Mr Maurice Newns, Mr Cyril E. Diamond, Mr C. W. Webb and the Reverend Roy W. Dooley.

Special thanks go to the staff of Northamptonshire Libraries, the County Record Office at Delapre Abbey, Northampton, Mr Alan Cleaver of the Peterborough Evening Telegraph, the ever helpful Mr Derek Phillips of the Peterborough City Museum and Art Gallery, and Mr R. C. Gill who allowed me to reproduce his late uncle's splendid drawings.

Help also came from Maurice and Joyce Palmer, Mr Arthur C. Smith, who loaned part of his collection of Harry Meyer photographs, Mr Nigel Moon, supplier of endless photographs and information, Mr Donald W. Muggeridge, who despatched his photographic negatives from America, and my good friend Mr Henry Wozniak, a true enthusiast who looks beyond the romance and into the technicalities of the subject.

Last but not least the people that helped to put it all together, including Mrs Diane Stokes and Ms Sara Warran, who typed and re-typed thousands of words, Mr A. J. George, who reproduced many of the photographs, and my publisher Mr Robert Wharton, who saw the potential in my pile of loose papers. Special thanks are due to Mr John Hardaker, whose skills in editing and production have proved invaluable. Final words must go to my wife Valerie whose support and encouragement are gratefully appreciated.

Foreword

Over the last twenty years or so there has been a revival of interest and activity in recording and preserving what is left of Britain's rural and industrial past. While ever increasing tracts of land are being threatened and taken over by housing developments, industrial parks, hypermarkets, theme parks and motorways, remaining old industrial sites and buildings are gradually overwhelmed and demolished. So it is increasingly essential that these old sites and structures are recorded in detail, and preserved where justifiably practical, before they disappear for ever without record.

Not least among such sites are those of the rural corn milling industry, and our windmills are perhaps some of its most vulnerable buildings. Their reduction in use and numbers became an established fact in the latter half of the nineteenth century as more efficient and economical milling processes were gradually introduced; it accelerated between the two world wars, and by the 1950s windmills had become practically out of use commercially.

In 1930 The Society for the Protection of Ancient Buildings formed a Windmill Section (later to include watermills) which, under the guidance of certain dedicated individuals, brought to public attention the importance and plight of the disappearing windmills, and pioneered their preservation. Around the same time a number of authors, notably R. Thurston Hopkins, W. Coles Finch, M. I. Batten, D. Smith and P. Hemming wrote books that were to become the early classics of windmill literature: and these were followed in the 1950s to the present day by more equally important books, surveys and papers on the subject by such authorities as Rex Wailes, K. G. Farries, M. T. Maston and others. Perhaps the most significant development was in the 1970s and 1980s when a number of mill groups and societies were formed in various counties, commencing in East Anglia and Kent, and eventually spreading to some of the Home Counties, the Midlands, Lincolnshire, Wales, the North West and parts of Southern England.

Northamptonshire does not have one of these county societies and was never a large traditional windmill area like, for instance, East Anglia, Lincolnshire and Kent, and scant attention has been paid to its windmills so far. Nevertheless the county did have a milling industry, and therefore it is important that its windmill heritage should be recorded before it is too late. Trevor Stainwright has made a timely and valuable contribution to windmill literature with his survey. His careful and detailed fieldwork and study of the subject, over a period of years, have been brought together in this book which provides us with the first comprehensive source of information on Northamptonshire windmills and their remains.

ARTHUR C. SMITH

Introduction

'... Northamptonshire is a home of lost windmills.' So wrote Stanley Freese in his book *In Search of English Windmills*, written between 1929 and 1930! Fifty years later when I began my researches no more than fourteen mills were left standing in the county. Another four could be found in the Soke of Peterborough, although since 1974 the area has been amalgamated with Cambridgeshire due to changes in the county boundaries.

In 1900 around fifty windmills remained standing in one form or another (it has been claimed as many as fifty-five existed this century, but at present I can only find evidence of forty-five.) Northamptonshire was rich in post mills during this period, and many were typical in having a single-storeyed roundhouse, with exceptions at Bozeat, Fengate in Peterborough, Naseby and Old. These were built as open trestle post mills. Common sails (mostly clockwise turning) were another distinctive feature, once again some exceptions being at Bozeat, Kettering and Barnack. Winding was carried out with tailpoles (no evidence of fantails has been found), sometimes, as in the cases of Bozeat and Byfield, with the added luxury of a cartwheel or winch.

Towards the end of the nineteenth century wind and water power had largely been superseded by more efficient means, and by the time of the First World War many mills had shut down. In the years preceding and just after the Great War a massive purge seems to have taken place and large numbers of Northamptonshire's post mills were felled. Amongst the victims were Badby, Barnack, Byfield, Clipston, Long Buckby, Naseby, Scaldwell and Weston-on-the-Welland. Others already derelict met dramatic ends in storms or by fire, such as Fengate, Little Weldon and Old.

Tower mills in the county were of a mixed collection varying in height and style. Some had ogee or dome-shaped caps, others were gabled. At East Haddon and Oundle the caps could be described as cone-shaped, while Brigstock tower mill and the smock mill at Eye boasted boat-type caps. Many carried fantails, a few of them tailpoles or luffing gear and chains. A fair number of towers were stone-built but just over half were constructed of brick. Sail arrangements, batters and number of floors also varied; in fact one could say that within Northamptonshire no two tower mills were the same. This could also be claimed of the only two smock mills that survived into the twentieth century, being at Eye Green near Peterborough, and Rushden, not far from the Bedfordshire border.

By the Second World War only two Peterborough mills were still grinding, the famous tall eight-sailer at Eye and the smaller tower at Werrington (which had the honour of being the county's last working windmill, eventually ceasing work in 1953.) Most of the surviving towers became house conversions typified by Kingsthorpe mill, Northampton (carried out at a time when working windmills were numerous) or Sulgrave mill (until 1981 just an empty shell.) However, there is a negative side to such practices, as illustrated by a once derelict tower mill situated in the Daventry area. In 1972 this mill was unique in still retaining the remnants of its cap, sails and machinery.

Instead of a programme of restoration the mill was sold off for house conversion, thereby robbing future generations forever of a piece of Northamptonshire's industrial history.

By the mid-seventies Northamptonshire was indeed a county of lost windmills. Thankfully not every county suffers the misfortunes that are represented here. Norfolk and Cambridgeshire are leading the field in restoration work, and let us hope others will learn by their example.

Windmills — the different types and how they work

This section is intended to give the reader a brief insight into the technicalities of the subject using photographs of existing mills in other counties, and drawings, to explain certain items of machinery. It must be said that this is merely a basic guide, and those seeking a more detailed understanding of windmills should refer to one of the water and windmill books listed in the bibliography. Other explanations are given in the general text where relevant.

The windmills found in Northamptonshire comprised the three basic types — post mills, smock mills and tower mills. The earliest of the three was the post mill, the main machinery of which was contained within the box-like body, or buck, mounted upon a single main post on which it could pivot. The post formed part of a trestle structure made up of two horizontal cross beams known as the crosstrees, the four ends of which sat upon brick piers. Four diagonally positioned quarterbars carried the weight of the post and buck, and were tenoned into the ends of the crosstrees.

Sometimes the trestle was left exposed, but quite often it was enclosed within a roundhouse. Turning the mill's body to face the correct wind direction was achieved by means of a tailpole. This was done manually, although in other counties many post mills were equipped with fantails. A development of the post mill was the smock mill, which differed from its predecessor in having a fixed tapered tower and a moveable cap containing the sail axle — the windshaft.

The smock tower was of wooden construction, standing upon a brick base, and was normally octagonal in plan, though some mills of this kind had six sides, in a few cases ten or twelve. Few smock mills were built in Northamptonshire, but a fair number survive elsewhere, especially in Kent. Sadly the smock mill proved somewhat vulnerable to damage compared with the post mill.*

A sturdier variation came in the form of the tower mill, another 'capped' mill, but this time built of brick or stone. A stronger structure meant that such mills could be built much larger to accommodate more equipment. Most of the surviving windmills found throughout Britain are tower mills, although many are no more than empty shells.

Sails and winding (or luffing)

Windmill sails (also known as sweeps) underwent various developments. The simplest type was the common sail, a lattice-like framework covered with cloth. The shuttered sail made its appearance in 1772 with the invention of the spring sail which made setting the sails much easier but retained the inconvenience of having to stop and adjust each sweep. This problem was solved in 1807 with the invention of the patent

*The Newcomen Society Transactions, 1959-60, vol. 32, p95, 'Some Windmill Fallacies' by Rex Wailes.

sail — again, a shuttered sail, but instead of a spring mechanism, the shutters were worked by a series of levers and cranks operated by a striking rod passing through the hollow windshaft. The striking rod projected from the rear of the windshaft and was

The open trestle post mill at Great Gransden, Cambridgeshire, displaying its post and supporting quarter bars. [Photo: The author]

coupled to a rack and pinion assembly worked by an external chain. The miller could thus adjust the sails while they were still in motion. The sailframes including the main timber, the whip, were bolted to stocks which were inserted through a box-like canister or poll end fixed to the end of the windshaft. An alternative to the poll end was the iron cross which also allowed a greater number of sweeps to be used.

Bringing the sails around to face the 'eye of the wind' — or winding — has been explained for post mills, but for the 'capped' mills it posed something of a problem. The tailpole method successful with post mills proved less than satisfactory for the smock and tower mills. The steep angle of the pole from the cap to the ground offered little leverage and some poles were fitted with winches to ease the task. A development of this was to install a winch in the cap area operated by an endless chain. The fully automatic winding gear came in 1745 with the invention of the fantail, a device set at right angles to the sails, mounted at the rear of the cap. Any change in the wind's direction caused the fantail to rotate and bring the cap and sails around to face the wind.

Machinery

Beneath the cap, fixed to the windshaft, was the brake wheel which engaged a horizontally set gear called the wallower, attached to an upright shaft. This passed vertically through the centre of the mill to where, at its base, was fixed the great spur wheel, often of similar construction to the brake wheel. The spur wheel drove up to four stone nuts powering the millstones via spindles or quants, depending on that particular mill's arrangement. Mill machinery could be of either timber or iron construction, but it was not unusual to find iron gears equipped with wooden teeth. Sometimes the great spur wheel drove the stones from above, sometimes from below. This was respectively known as overdrift and underdrift.

A similar system was also used in post mills but an earlier arrangement involved the brake wheel driving a pair of stones, situated on the top floor, directly from a stone

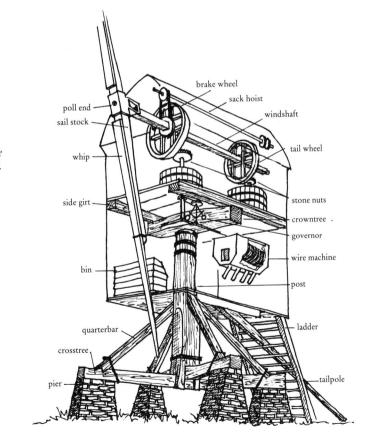

A cutaway drawing of the workings of a post mill.

The poll-end or cannister of Lutton-Gowts tower mill, Lincolnshire. The casting housed the sail stocks to which the whips were bolted. [Photo: The author]

Four sail whips at Wrawby post mill, Humberside, are clamped to an iron cross which dispensed with sail stocks and, in some cases, allowed a greater number of sweeps to be mounted. In Wrawby's case these are spring sails with the boxes on the whip housing the springs. [Photo: The author]

Brake and tail wheel system with stones mounted in tandem. This arrangement is known to have been used at Kettering and Long Buckby.

The unique system of the Bozeat post mill, with the brake wheel behind the wallower and stones.

Rear view of a mill with stones side by side, driven by the wallower, great spur wheel and stone nuts.

15

nut. Often the process was repeated at the rear of the post mill by means of a tailwheel fitted to the opposite end of the windshaft.

Millstones were usually mounted in pairs with the top stone, the runner stone, revolving above the static bedstone. Of the two types found in the county both were very common: Derbyshire peaks, suitable for coarse grain such as barley, and French burrs, for fine work (i.e. wheat for flour). Grooves or furrows in the stones ensured that the grain falling between them was cut rather than crushed, and allowed the cut

Willingham smock mill, Cambridgeshire, with two patent sails in need of repair. Note how the striking rod (part of the striking gear that operated the sail shutters) passes through the poll-end, and the windshaft to the rear of the mill.
[Photo: The author]

grain (meal) to pass outside the stones for the next phase.

The tentering gear employed a governor to regulate the distance between the millstones and prevented the runner stone rising as the revolutions increased. Bridgetrees supported the stone spindle (upon which the runner stone pivoted).

Dressers

Any produce naturally had to be filtered in an effort to separate flour from bran and to

Barnack mill's clasp-arm brake wheel, fixed to the hollow wooden windshaft. Encircling the wheel is the brake shoe. [Photo: The author]

The governor, stone nut and great spur wheel of the underdrift 'Shades Mill', Soham, Cambridgeshire. [Photo: The author]

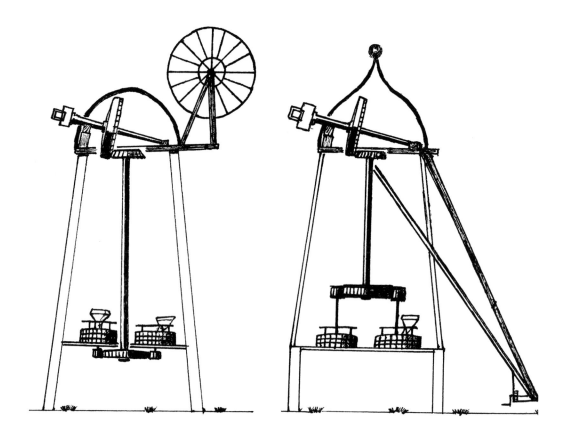

Underdrift. Stones driven from below, as in this example of a tower mill (with a dome cap and fantail).

Overdrift. Stones driven from above, as in this example of a smock mill (with an ogee cap and tailpole).

remove grit or foreign bodies. This was made possible with the introduction of flour dressers. Two of the most common types were the bolter and the improved wire machine which were driven by bevelled gears and sometimes indirectly belt driven. Other variations included smutters and grain cleaners.

Auxiliary power

During the latter half of the nineteenth century many millers employed steam engines (either stationary or portable) to assist with grinding. These were usually brought in to power a single stone pair, sometimes two, via an external pulley.

PART I

Windmills in Northamptonshire

The Old Mill, Badby.

BADBY POST MILL

Apart from the Soke of Peterborough, the greatest concentration of remains of windmills within Northamptonshire are located in the western part of the county in the Daventry area. The site of one of them was at Badby where, until the early years of the Great War, a post mill stood at Bare Hill Farm, one quarter of a mile west of the village, itself two miles south of Daventry.

The mill's date of construction is not known for certain as it is absent from the Eyre and Jefferys county map of 1779, and does not appear on the Greenwood and Co. map of 1825/26. A post mill symbol headed 'Windmill' can be found upon the 1834 first edition Ordnance Survey map. Also mentioned is 'Bare Hill House' instead of 'Farm'.

The post mill could be clearly seen from the Daventry to Banbury road (now the A361) standing on the left hand side of a track leading to the farm. In appearance Badby mill was typical of the post mills that stood within Northamptonshire. The buck (body) was clad in wide, horizontally laid weather boarding, possibly being extended rearwards at some time during its working life. The breast of the mill may have been boarded in a similar fashion, but was later given the added protection of a covering of tarred felt sheets, as was the roof. Small hatch-type windows also featured and, continuing in the Northamptonshire tradition, four cloth-covered common sails drove the wooden machinery. Winding the mill was undertaken manually by use of a tailpole. Steep steps with a single banister led up to stable-type double doors. The petticoat (if any) at the base of the buck is missing in later pictures of the mill. A single storey brick roundhouse protected the trestle structure from the elements, but did not actually carry the weight of the mill body, although the brick piers upon which the crosstrees rested were probably incorporated into the walls of the roundhouse. The external wall was encircled by two parallel iron bands adding stability to the structure, and the wooden roof of the roundhouse was protected, as with other parts of the mill, by a covering of tarred felt.

Prior to 1847 there is no mention of any millers at Badby within the pages of the county trade directories. Kelly's of that year records Mr George Douglas as the miller. He is listed in Slater's Directory of 1850 and Kelly's 1854. In Melvill's 1861 edition George Douglas, jun., is reported to be the miller as well as being a farmer and maltster. George Douglas, sen., was operating again at Badby according to Slater's volume of 1862. Two years later Mr Douglas was listed as a farmer and maltster only. This was repeated in the Royal Directory of 1866, although Badby had been interpreted as 'Bradby'. Other trade manuals were consulted to build up an interesting picture of events. In Harrods' Directory of 1876 Mr William Green was listed as undertaking the milling business. Between the years 1869 and 1871 he had been documented as a shopkeeper. After 1876 there were no more references to any millers at Badby. William Green was later to be described as a farmer, shopkeeper, and in 1890 a 'higgler'.

During its years of abandonment the post mill was portrayed by a number of artists.   Frank C. Gill included two of his sketches of the mill in an article which appeared in the *Northampton County Magazine* of 1928.   The work was entitled 'The Vanishing Windmill' and told of the decline of windpower, using Northamptonshire as an example.   His first drawing, made in 1900, depicted the post mill in an almost complete state.   However, the second one dated 1910 shows a sail broken at mid-point — this seeming to be the only damage.   Another artist, the talented J. A. Perrin, sketched and later painted the derelict post mill.   Both pictures are held at the central library in Northampton.   Executed in February 1915 Mr Perrin's view showed the mill to be in a very poor condition.   Many treads were missing from the ladder, and the weather boarding had broken away in places.   It was the common sails that had suffered the worst of the neglect.   In the painting one can see the remnants of one broken sweep, while of the other only the stock and part of the whip remain.   A photograph taken at the time shows the mill at a different angle where the damage is more evident.   One of the sail stocks had slipped allowing the whip to fall into contact with the ground.   Just visible in the photograph, but more so in the Perrin painting, is a small dormer type extension in the roof, level with the brake wheel.

Sadly, in the same year as Perrin's visit, the old post mill was demolished.   In 1944 Herbert E. S. Simmons inspected the site and wrote that not even a mound was left.

Many years later, in May 1981, the author and a friend visited Bare Hill Farm in the hope of gleaning information.   There were no signs of life in the house.   In fact, the whole farm seemed deserted, so we took advantage of the opportunity for a look round.   Half a peak stone was discovered acting as a doorstep to an outbuilding, and a quarter piece of another was found near a barn.   We took the liberty of peering inside

One half of a peak stone employed as a doorstep to a barn. [Photo: The author]

Badby mill in 1900 by F.C. Gill. [Reproduced with permission of R.C. Gill]

its dark interior where my companion pointed out a large roof beam, suggesting that it could have come from the old mill. Darkness prevented detailed examination, but it seemed feasible at the time.

While making our way back to my car we pinpointed the actual mill site, now no more than a slight rise rather than a mound. Later we toured the village. The local pub is known as 'The Windmill', although the painting on its sign was that of a tower mill [happily, replaced in 1989 by a post mill painting]. An elderly man invited us into his hall to show us a small table made from some of the post mill's timber. It is probable that other pieces may still exist within the village. Before we left I noticed that the shell of Newnham tower mill (see page 91) could be seen from his front door.

BARBY TOWER MILL

Four and a half miles north-west of Daventry, at a crossroads, is part of an old lane which many decades ago eventually led to Rugby. The lane, now a public footpath to Barby Wood, borders a meadow where, upon a mound, are the remains of Barby tower mill. The footpath is opposite the Welton road which crosses the Willoughby road and leads past a water tower to the village of Barby, half a mile north-east of the mill.

When visited and photographed in detail in 1981, Barby windmill stood empty and alone. To its north-western side a heap of rubble was all that remained of a boiler house. Originally built as a separate building, and yet so close that it could have been mistaken for an extension of the mill added at a later date. At the opposite side of the tower, a few yards away, remained the fallen framework of a dome roof that replaced its original cap. The roof, built of sheet iron, had a radius of 8 feet 6 inches, implying that at the curb the tower's diameter would have been 17 feet.

The mill is three storeys in height, built of red brick and lacking any protective tarring. At the base the wall thickness measures 21 inches, while the base diameter is approximately 23 feet. Until recently there were no doors or windowpanes, many having been bricked up. The ground floor is particularly interesting for, as well as the two opposing doorways, a third has been knocked out in the north-eastern wall. The author believes this was a later introduction, probably to compensate for the north-western entrance being bricked up long ago. It was this wall that backed on to the pile of bricks, once the boiler house seemingly demolished some time ago, as a barbed wire fence erected around the rubble was down and covered with weeds.

Traces of brick flooring could be found within, but most of the floor was earth, churned up over the years by many farm animals. A fireplace on the ground floor had also been bricked up. To the right of this an iron picket ring fixed into the brickwork was the only metal item left in the mill. First and second storey flooring beams were present, but they were not the original ones. Other woodwork included the curb, most of which was still in place. Internally, at dust floor level, five out of six timbers remained fixed from the curb to the tops of the four window apertures. These were estimated to be between 18 inches and 2 feet in length and two or three inches square. Some damage at the top of the tower was noticeable, and many bricks littered the site, as did debris from the fallen roof, but it is a pleasant area with two large ponds and much marshland at the far end of the field.

Known as 'Berby' on a county map dated 1610, the village formed part of the Favsley Hundred. Apart from churches, no other buildings were marked on the map. A windmill is depicted at Barby on the Eyre and Jefferys county map of 1779. A local man told the author that it was his belief this was an earlier windmill which stood in the same area but not on the same site, and the tower mill succeeded it. The tower mill does appear on the Ordnance Survey map of 1835, and a detailed map of the village, with a scale of 25 inches to one mile, referred to the site as 'The Meadow'.

Barby tower mill in 1970, showing dome roof and boiler house. [Photo: Nigel Moon]

Known locally as 'Millfield', the area is recorded as 'Plot 112' with 5,959 acres. The map, published in 1900, is held by a local man who, despite my requests, preferred to remain nameless. He told me that throughout most of its working life the mill was operated by two men, Mr E. Hart and Mr G. Eagles. Herbert E. S. Simmons recorded Mr Hart at the windmill as early as 1828, but their names do appear in the 1847, 1854, 1864 and 1869 editions of the trade directories. The last miller was a Mr Smith, whose grandson still lives in the village and runs a local store. Sadly he was unable to give any information about his grandfather other than that he was the miller.

During my second visit to the mill on 15 March 1987 I encountered a farmhand shepherding sheep in the meadow. He told me that his father, who would have been 95 years old had he still been alive, had remembered the mill working. The shepherd also supplied much information about the owners of the mill.

No photographs have been discovered of the windmill during its working life, but I was told that it did work with four sails. Unfortunately, in the 1870s they were blown off during a storm. The fan also came down about this time, but whether it was a victim of the gale or removed as a result of it is not known. Later the headframe was taken down, along with the windshaft and brake wheel. The fallen sails remained by the mill for many years before being sold along with most of the machinery, but not before the mill underwent a dramatic change.

A shallow dome roof replaced the original cap, and a single storey boiler house with a high pitched roof was built on to the tower's north-western wall. Within this a second-hand steam driven engine was installed. Unfortunately, the system of drive

Barby tower mill in 1981. Only a shell remains. The rubble of the boiler house can just be seen to the right of the picture. [Photo: The author]

from below instead of above did not work well in this particular mill. The timber machinery needed constant repair, and naturally constituted a great deal of expenditure. In the end this was responsible for the mill's closure just after the turn of the century, and throughout the next few decades it remained idle but not alone. The tower became a haven for rats. Drawn to the mill during its working life, in search of grain, dozens of them established their lairs there long after it ceased to work. Not only was the windmill infested with them, but also the boiler house and even the engine itself.

It was during 1937 that enthusiast G. N. Shann visited Barby mill, and in his brief account, preserved in the Herbert Simmons papers, Shann claimed that much of his information had come from the Rector of Barby. The Reverend Richard Stovin Mitchison MA owned various properties within the village, including the tower mill and the meadow. It was during this time that the millfield became something of an attraction for local people. Cricket was often played there, and two large ponds, once brick quarries, also proved popular. Concerned with the safety aspect, a sign was erected in an effort to deter people from swimming. Some time later the Reverend generously offered the land around the mill to the Parish as a sports field. Curiously, the locals refused it, but nevertheless cricket matches continued to be played there.

The war clouds of World War II covered Barby in 1940 with the much feared 'Invasion of Britain' threat. The creating of the Local Defence Volunteers, later renamed the Home Guard, gave many too old, too young or unfit the chance to take an active part in the war. Reverend Mitchison became Commanding Officer of the local unit and, not lacking in spirit of duty, his wife was a head member of the area ARP. The enterprising rector donated the tower mill for war use as an observation post, but before it was fit for service certain modifications had to be made. Many openings within the tower wall had been bricked up years before, so four square holes were knocked out just above the line of the second floor windows. Replacement flooring was also installed, the supporting beams being cemented into the original mortices. The obsolete steam engine was subsequently dismantled and removed.

Meanwhile, the windmill's owner, Reverend Mitchison, was still heavily involved with military activities. According to a local man, his platoon often set up road blocks, and during one such check a convoy of army lorries was halted. When the rector questioned the Service Corps driver of the leading truck he was met with a hail of abuse. Exactly what was said is unknown, but it was enough to make the Reverend resign his commission some time afterwards.

After the war the mill was sold to a Mr Johnson, and some time later it passed to a Mr Hinkley. He held the mill for twenty years before Mr A. Eden purchased it in the late 1960s/early 1970s. The gear, which still littered the site,* was sold off. It is claimed that this included a great deal of 'iron work'. In the meantime the tower and the boiler house were used for storage, and it was in that condition when seen and photographed by Nigel Moon in 1970. Some time afterwards the boiler house was demolished and the remains fenced off. In 1978 a gale sent the dome roof crashing to the ground. This, too, remained where it fell for many years. Very little of the roof was left in 1981. By 1987 there was nothing.

In 1974 the Barby Parish Council published a village survey. In a section devoted to buildings worthy of preservation was listed 'XIV The Old Mill, Daventry Road'. When the survey was drawn up no other buildings apart from the Church were listed. It may be of interest to know that the population of the village in 1974 was 1,185. Just after Mr Eden died in 1983 the windmill was put up for auction along with 70 acres of land. It was described in the sale as a 'well-known landmark standing at over 550 feet above sea level'. 'Lot 3' was purchased by a firm of builders who subsequently improved the structure by adding a flat roof, windows and doors. The tower is now used as a store, and the mill field has been divided in two by means of a barbed wire fence.

*Local intelligence insists that some remnants of gear remained on the site until the mid to late 1960s.

BLAKESLEY MILL
Built in 1832 by Francis Welch
now used as a store

Blakesley tower mill in 1899 by F.C. Gill. The same year that this drawing was made, the mill was partly dismantled. [Reproduced with permission of R.C. Gill]

BLAKESLEY TOWER MILL

Situated in a field at the end of a row of houses is the five storey, semi-crenellated tower of Blakesley windmill. Lacking cap and sails, the structure is adjacent to a number of outbuildings full of various farm implements, and naturally the tower has also been employed as a store. Contained within the sheds are a number of tractors dating from the 1950s-60s period. Although far from being restored they, along with as many spare parts that room will allow, are collected by Mr Charlie Burbridge who rents the windmill from Mr N. Locke. Few valuables are kept within the mill since it was broken into by vandals who gained entry through a ground floor window and smashed the strip lights fitted to the ground floor ceiling.

Most of the ladders still exist, as do many of the sack traps, noted during the author's exploration of the mill. The first floor, in common with the others, is empty of machinery and stones, but two upright supporting posts are clearly original, as is a nearby meal chute. Upon the second floor two doorways existed, reminding us that they once led out to a wide stage, of which no trace remains. The western doorway has been bricked up and throughout this mill various windows along with one of the two ground floor doorways have suffered a similar fate. An unusual find was the fireplace at the southern part of the wall. Four more upright posts, one of them at least complete with a bridge-tree, support what was once the stone floor.

At this point I was advised not to venture any higher as the floor timbers were said to be in a very dangerous condition. Torn between curiosity and the wish not to offend my host waiting two storeys below, I risked a quick peep at the next level. This, the third floor, is totally empty, as is the fourth, with the exception of a central ladder to the flat roof; the former being a modification dating from the last war. Outside, entrance to the mill is gained by climbing a number of steps to the raised threshold, a useful platform for loading carts. Above the entrance is a date stone which reads: 'Francis Welsh built AD 1832'.

The Maidford brick of which the mill was constructed was never given a protective coating of tar. As a result the brickwork has softened. Indeed, it is claimed that blue tits and other birds have made nests in the internal wall by constantly pecking at it.

During its working life Blakesley tower mill, often referred to as 'Quinbury End Mill', stood six storeys in height and carried a dome cap, four anti-clockwise sails, and a fantail. It was built and run by Mr Francis Welsh who lived, near the village green at the Dower House, a one-time farmhouse and home for widows. He was a keen angler and when not at work Mr Welsh could be found fishing at Canons Ashby in the company of Frank Loydell and Richard Bray, the Postmaster of Blakesley.

It is likely that one of Francis's relations was Tom Welsh, the noted county cricketer of the late nineteenth century. This, too, would have been about the time when the windmill stopped work. For a few years it was left in a state of total abandonment until 1899 when the cap, sails and all the machinery were removed. The tower itself was truncated by one floor and the walls were subsequently

A cutaway sketch of Blakesley mill as it appeared in 1989, with two upright posts on the first floor, and four posts and a fireplace on the second.

crenellated. Not long afterwards Francis Welsh, then well into his nineties, died.

No photographs of the complete mill have as yet been unearthed, but a drawing of it produced in 1899, the same year as its alteration, appeared in the *Northampton County Magazine* of 1928. The artist and author was Frank C. Gill, and his article 'The Vanishing Windmill' included descriptions of other Northamptonshire mills. Mr Gill's illustration of Blakesley tower mill depicted it in a ruinous condition with only one shuttered sail intact, and only the stocks of two others visible. The fantail was absent, but Gill's drawing had included a fan stage and a petticoat beneath the cap.

Within the text Frank had described the second floor stage as being used to set sail cloths, perhaps emphasizing that the mill worked with both common and shuttered sails. The same picture featured in P. B. Kingston's book *Blakesley* recounting the history of the village in photographs. Phil Kingston is a life-long vehicle enthusiast, and for many years he ran the garage near the mill, and has owned a number of classic cars. Phil has also contributed to the now sadly missed *Old Motor* magazine. His memories can be found in a 1972 edition (vol. II, no. 6). Apart from his cars Phil

Blakesley mill in summer 1989, 90 years after the cap, sails and top floor were removed.
[Photo: The author]

Kingston has a general love of local history, as is verified by the section of stained glass window gracing his living room. It is one of a few relics from the now demolished Blakesley Hall. From the living room Phil has a pleasing view of the tower mill, and he recalled its past with ease. 'During the 1930s Charlie Burbridge's father-in-law used the mill as a tool store. The top part of it was used as a hay loft, and the sack hoist (said to be the original modified to suit) took the hay to the top.'

By the end of the decade Britain was at war and the subsequent air raids over Coventry and the north meant that German bombers often flew over the county. A chain of Observer Corps posts had been set up and the group covering Blakesley selected the windmill as a suitable vantage point. A few modifications were carried out on the tower, such as the central ladder positioned on the fourth floor. From here the Corps members could gain entry to the crenellated top which proved to be most unpopular as the men were subjected to the cold wind. To rectify this the castellations were filled in on the eastern half of the tower.

After the war the mill reverted back to its use as a store, but its proximity to the houses makes it an appealing candidate for home conversion. This possibility was investigated by Mr D. W. Winkles, nephew of the last miller of Wootton windmill (see page 139). Fortunately (or not, depending upon one's point of view) the scheme was not pursued, but at some future date the prospect is bound to be looked into again, despite the tower's poor condition. However, potential buyers will have to brave the windmill's protectors in the shape of Charlie Burbridge and Phil Kingston.

Bozeat post mill.

BOZEAT POST MILL

During the last century two windmills were thought to have stood at Bozeat. To the north of the village was a post mill in a farmyard upon the left-hand side of the Wollaston road. The second windmill was also a post mill, sited upon the western side of the road to Olney. The north mill was depicted upon the first Ordnance Survey map of the district, the 'Old Series' one-inch map of about 1833. The southern mill was not, nor did either mill appear, on the Eyre and Jefferys map of North-amptonshire which was first published in 1779. This is curious because the south mill is said to have had the initials and date: 'R. H. 1761' inscribed upon its 2 foot 8 inch square main post. The northern windmill had disappeared by 1846 when the other was offered for sale with the inducement that: 'there is no other windmill within six miles'. It is now believed that they were in fact the same mill having been originally built at the northern location, then between 1833 and 1846 sold, dismantled, and re-erected on the southern site.

Bozeat's was the most famous of all the Northamptonshire windmills and was the last post mill in the county to work and stand. Photographs and accounts of it have appeared in innumerable studies, including a brief reference which appeared in the book 'History of Cornmilling - Volume 2: Watermills and Windmills' by Richard Bennett and John Elton (first published in 1899 and republished in 1973) where they described the mill as being 'thoroughly ancient in type, but perfectly modern in equipment'. This view was understandable as Bozeat mill had an open trestle; the post, upon and about which the body or 'buck' turned, was supported by four inclined quarterbars, each seven feet long, which took the whole of the building's weight. The lower ends of the quarterbars were tenoned into mortises at the outer ends of a pair of large horizontal cross-trees positioned perpendicularly to each other beneath the post. The crosstrees were each twenty feet long and their ends rested upon four brick piers. The building was 35 feet high and bore both common and double shuttered patent sails turning in a clockwise direction. At the end of its long tailpole it had fixed a large wheel and winch. This, when hand-cranked, would turn the mill into the wind. The trestle and buck structures mainly consisted of oak, but the sail stocks and whips were of Norwegian pine. One of the most unusual features of the buck was its outward appearance; the breast projected forwards at its foot and was inclined backwards and tapered as it ascended to the top, mainly to accommodate its irregular machinery arrangement. The brake wheel had its toothed side facing towards the sails and the wallower forward of it. Two pairs of grindstones were mounted in the bottom floor upon hurst frames, these being overdriven. This meant that there must have been an upright shaft and a great spur wheel.

In 1846 Thomas Saunders held the mill, but was soon replaced by William Spencer. By 1851 Mr Denton Gilbert of Pudding Bag Lane had taken over together with his single employee William Skevington, the 21-year-old son of the village baker. John Walker, a 41-year-old Bedfordshire miller had taken charge of the post mill by 1871.

Bozeat post mill in 1934. In the above left hand picture note the felt covered breast of the mill, and the steam mill in the background. Below is the hand-cranked winding gear, now minus the cartwheel.
[Photos: Donald Muggeridge]

Mr Walker had formerly worked the watermill at Milton Ernest, and the post mills at Riseley and Yeldon (or Yielden as is preferred by local people). He is also believed to have run the watermill at Billing near Northampton. Walker's oldest son John, then 23, assisted in the work along with 20-year-old George Hooton. At some time between 1877 and 1890 Mr Walker sold the mill to John Monk who in turn sold it to another John, this time John Little. Mr Little, together with his daughter and a handful of employees, was the last of the village's millers. The family came from Hertfordshire where John had formerly held the watermill at Hunton Bridge near Watford. John Little employed two workers: Percy Patrick from Easton and William Monk, thought to have been John Monk's son. A third man, Mr Morditt, attended to the horses and pigs. Stone dressing was carried out by either Mr Little or occasionally by 'Old Jimmy' Elliott from Wellingborough. Later William Monk took up the art himself.

Many of the details which follow were recalled by Miss Mabel Little, the last miller's daughter, who had assisted her father with the operation of the windmill and the adjacent steam mill. Mabel recalled that the windmill was more heavily used during the winter months, after harvest, but Miss Little could not say if it had ever worked at night. She remembered a persistent problem which plagued many millers: rats. A dog and several cats were introduced to combat them.

For many years the windmill ground grist for cattle, and in a steady wind was said to be capable of grinding about twenty quarters of grist per day. In addition to the grist, the windmill produced stone-ground flour, for which the customers included many local farmers as well as the gentry.

During the time that John Walker operated the post mill a vicious storm at Bozeat damaged its sails. Miss Little remembered that even in a light wind she could distinctly feel the mill rocking when on the top floor. Around 1914 the windmill was in need of some repairs. These were undertaken by a firm of millwrights — Course & Sons of Bedford — but the mill ceased to work soon afterwards. However, Mr Little continued to work the steam mill until the Second World War.

Towards the end of its lifetime the windmill received many visitors, often picnickers, who were always asked to leave. Others included Stanley Freese, who was to record its destruction. Another was Donald Muggeridge whose photographs accompany this account. The late Mr Rex Wailes of the Society for the Protection of Ancient Buildings also paid many visits to Bozeat. In 1932, on 28 May, Wailes inspected the mill in the interests of possible preservation. Generally its condition was far from satisfactory. The trestle had suffered from years of neglect, and the crosstrees and quarterbars were rife with decay. Although some protective measures had been taken, such as plating and tarring, the mill's future seemed to be very bleak. The body, too, had deteriorated to an alarming extent. Hardly any weather boarding was without signs of considerable rot.

Mr Wailes also reported that the ladder and tailpole were in an extremely precarious state. The sails had also been badly damaged through the years, and many of the shutters from the patent sails were missing. Inside the buck, rot had invaded the roof spars and some of the mechanism including the hoppers and the wire machine flour dresser. However, the main beams, the flooring and the crowntree were unaffected. Some thought had been given to the crowntree because it had been clad with lead plating. In his 1932 report, Rex Wailes estimated that between £200 and

Bozeat mill in the late thirties. The deterioration is plainly evident. [Photo: Mabel Little]

£300 would have been needed to put the mill into good repair, but no money was ever found for the work. As one would expect, the inevitable happened. During the night of 28 February/1 March 1949 in steady but light rain — by no means a storm, said Miss Little (which conflicts with newspaper reports), the tottering remains of Northamptonshire's last post windmill came crashing to the ground. The most casual inspection revealed the cause: a hole 'big enough to hold a bag of cement' had rotted into one of the quarterbars which had given way.

The remains were cleared by the Wolverton District Council. Some salvaged parts, including the main post and brake wheel, found their way to the mill paddock at Bradwell, Buckinghamshire, where a three storey tower windmill has been reinstated

[Photo above: Evening Telegraph]

Aftermath of the storm which destroyed the county's last post mill at Bozeat in 1949.

[Photo below: Mabel Little]

in recent years. Photographs show the main post outside Bradwell Mill during 1955. But, sadly, the windshaft, crowntree and the inscribed main post were later stolen from the paddock, according to Stanley Freese. The brake wheel was left behind and it was thought to be still stored inside the tower during the early 1980s.

In 1954 the land upon which the windmill had stood was sold to the Wellingborough Rural District Council. A year later the disused steam mill was pulled down, and the former mill house followed in 1956. In the meantime Miss Little continued to live in Mill Road, Bozeat, in a Council-owned house built upon the land formerly belonging to the mill property. In her garden was a section of a large timber from the post mill. Some stones remained on the site until 18 March 1985 when the village's Historical and Archaeological Society recovered them and transferred them to the grounds of the local school. A JCB was used to transport the peak stones under the supervision of the Society's secretary — Mr David Stafferton. The mill stones can be seen there today, as the school's emblem is the windmill. Sadly Miss Little did not live to see this, as she died earlier in that year.

BRAUNSTON TOWER MILL

The unmistakable shape of Braunston tower mill can easily be seen from the village outskirts along with the steeple of the parish church. Both buildings are within a short distance of each other in the western part of Braunston. No doubt in days gone by it was the windmill that dominated the local landscape, perhaps being visible from the Grand Union Canal, if not the adjoining Oxford Canal. It then stood between seven and eight storeys high (the line of windows suggests seven, but an early newspaper report claims eight), and it was one of the tallest of the county's windmills to survive into the twentieth century. Even at its present six storeys Braunston mill still retains that honour, dwarfing the existing tall tower mills at Barnack (in the Soke of Peterborough) and Blakesley, by one floor.

Unlike these mills, Braunston has been converted into a four bedroom dwelling

Braunston mill before the First World War. Although the sails and stage have gone, the tower still carries its cap. [Photo: County Record Office]

Braunston mill as it appeared in 1938, with its crenellated top. This photograph is a combination of two pictures.
[Photo: H. Meyer]

Another pre-war view, this time showing the 'portcullised' windows. Note the small circular window between the fourth and fifth storeys.
[Photo: H. Meyer]

with luxuries such as central heating provided by an oil-fired boiler. When entering, one is greeted by the sight of the original beams exposed in the ceiling, as well as a showpiece of metal gearing complete with apple-wood teeth. At this level the internal diameter of the building is around 24 feet. Upon the first floor is the kitchen and dining room, while the landing boasts a doorway to an external balcony with steps descending to the ground. The second floor is devoted to the lounge, complete with fireplace. Here the diameter is 22 feet 6 inches. Pine steps lead to the third floor which comprises two bedrooms and a bathroom. At fourth floor level is the third of the bedrooms and a second balcony providing an excellent view of the village. The remaining bedroom is located upon the fifth and final storey, the diameter of which is

18 feet 6 inches. A large garden, twin garages and car port make this a very desirable property and a credit to Mr A. R. Lane who carried out many of the alterations during the late 1960s and early 1970s.

Constructed about 1800, the tower mill was one of two windmills that operated within the district, the second mill being situated on the Welton road in an area known as Little Braunston. The new tower mill was built of red brick with a stage at its fourth floor. A conical cap of unusual design topped the massive structure, unusual for its featured dormers fore and aft, the larger of the two at the rear where a luffing wheel was located. The four sails were said to have been 'cloth covered' and Stanley Freese once described it as a 'Fantailed tower', although no other proof has as yet been uncovered by the author to substantiate the claim. Other details are recorded in a sale notice which appeared in *The Warwick Advertiser* of 17 February 1816. It stated that the windmill contained three stone sets including a pair of French burrs with diameters of 5 feet, a pair of peaks at 4 feet 2 inches, and another set of burrs also measuring 4 feet 2 inches. Other equipment consisted of a 'bean mill' and 'two 4 foot machines'. The advertisement went on to report that the mill was 'with two tenements in the occupations of Joseph Middleton, William Woodhams and Robert Chambers'. Richard Bowers was listed as the miller in Pigot's 1830 Directory, while the 1840 edition documented Mr Bowers working alongside Richard Dodd. It seems Mr Dodd's contribution to milling was short-lived, for by 1847 he was described as a

The castellated tower in 1963.
[Photo: Nigel Moon]

Braunston mill in 1970 after the removal of the top floor. [Photo: Maurice and Joyce Palmer]

baker, and was later recorded as a grocer and confectioner. Richard Bowers, in the meantime, continued with the running of the windmill with help from relatives, John and later Henry Bowers. By 1874 the mill had passed to Braunston's last miller, Mr James Stubbs, possibly a relation of the local surgeon, William Stubbs, MD. James employed at least one assistant named Branston, who had a tragic accident at the mill. While on the stage the unfortunate Mr Branston was struck and killed by one of the rotating sails. Such was the force of the blow that the dead man's body was thrown into the churchyard.

It has been suggested that Mr Stubbs continued to run the windmill until about 1900, but it is much more likely it ceased work during the early 1890s, perhaps before. No Braunston millers are recorded in the 1894 and 1898 trade directories, and by 1905 the mill had lost its sails and stage. After the First World War all the machinery was removed and the cap taken down. The then owner, builder Mr Johnson, is rumoured to have abandoned his original intention to demolish the structure, claiming it was 'too tough a job'. Instead, the tower was put to use as a store for building materials. Mr Johnson subsequently erected crenellations on top of the tower, and strengthened the window lintels. This resulted in all the windows above third floor level being given a portcullised look.

After use by the local Home Guard during the war the tower was visited by Herbert E. S. 'Syd' Simmons, who also took the opportunity to interview Mr Johnson. At that time (1945) Mr Johnson still occupied the cottage which is believed to have

The same view as on page 41, in 1980 after the installation of the dome roof originally made for a grain silo. [Photo: The author]

been the original millhouse. Syd learned that the builder had personally undertaken the alterations, but unfortunately these had not included a great deal of internal maintenance. Materials were stored only on the first three storeys as the upper floors were considered to be unsafe. The owner claimed he was the son of the last miller, but it is much more likely that his father was an assistant to Mr Stubbs.

The 1960s proved to be the decade of change for the old mill, and many varied proposals were put forward for its future use. One unsuccessful idea, suggested in 1966, was to convert the tower into a 'sauna-sun clinic'. This was rejected by Daventry Rural District Council in September the same year. Another scheme which involved turning the windmill into a cafe, known as 'The Miller's Kitchen', did materialize, but seems to have been short-lived. Eventually the property was purchased by Mr Lane, who completely transformed the interior, making it habitable. By this time the tower stood six storeys high with a flat roof located three feet below the level of the brickwork. During the early 1970s a new dome roof, originally made for a grain silo, was fitted, and now the occupants can enter beneath the dome through a trap door.

My thanks go to Braunston historian Mr Leslie W. Herne and the venerable Mr Lane.

Byfield mill a few years before its destruction. Suggestions are that the bonfire in the foreground was to celebrate the coronation of George V in 1911. [Photo: Janet Blake]

BYFIELD POST MILL

One of the many post mills once dotted around the western half of the county, Byfield mill stood half a mile south of the village near a crossroads. It was a well known landmark, probably due to its proximity to a tollgate, and later the East and West Junction Railway which passed between the village and the mill site. It was one of two windmills that existed within the parish, an earlier example having once stood at the northern end of the village in an area still known to this day as 'Windmill Banks'.

This mill was said by molinologist G. N. Shann in 1937 to have been of 'some antiquity' as coins dating from the time of King Richard II (1367-1400) were found within its walls. Neither of the two Byfield mills was featured upon the Eyre and Jefferys map of 1779, but the southern windmill appeared on Bryant's 1824-26 map and the 1834 Ordnance Survey as 'Byfield Mill'. The latter was typical of the kind of post mill found throughout Northamptonshire during that period, with its horizontally boarded buck and single storey roundhouse. The roundhouse roof, breast and roof of the buck were protected from the elements by a covering of tarred felt. Four anticlockwise turning common sails were manually winded by a tailpole fitted with a cartwheel at the pole's end. The main post, which carried the weight of the whole mill, bore the inscription 'DL 1820' and possibly referred to the date of its erection.

One of the first to be associated with the windmill was Joseph Watkins who operated it for many years. J. & E. Watkins are recorded as Byfield millers in the 1847 and 1854 trade directories, but only J. Watkins is listed by 1864. Others who worked the mill included Mr T. Boot, possibly the Bush family who also ran a grocery and wine selling business, and John Elliman during the 1870s and 1880s. Shortly afterwards Elliman was replaced by a local farmer, John Henry Bromley, a well respected member of the community, being a major landowner and Chairman of the Byfield and District Working Men's Conservative Club.

Mr Bromley's granddaughter, Mrs Janet Blake, still lives in the village and is sadly the last in a family line whose roots can be traced back as far as the twelfth century. This is perhaps something of a cruel irony as John Henry was father to no less than fifteen children; six girls and nine boys. At least one of the sons died at a very early age but the tragedy did not prevent the strict upbringing of the rest of the family. No doubt the sons aided their father on the farm, with other assistance coming from waggoner and groom Martin Tredwell. Another employee was Thomas Richard 'Dicky' Jordan Billson, who is thought to have helped with the running of the windmill.

One of the 'tricks of the trade' that may have been adopted by Messrs Bromley or Billson (according to Shann) was to tie a horse to the end of the tailpole enabling the mill to be brought into wind with a minimum of effort. Mr Billson was often recorded as a farmer in the trade directories, while John Henry was catalogued as the miller in the 1894, 1898, 1903 and 1906 editions. In the 1910 volume Bromley was

Byfield post mill showing signs of neglect, especially to the roundhouse. The miller, John Henry Bromley, is standing nearest the sails, and next to him is Police Sergeant Haynes. [Photo: Janet Blake]

listed only as a landowner and farmer, leaving one with the assumption that by this time the windmill had stopped work. Although derelict, the buck and sails remained in a fair condition, while the roundhouse fell into a ruinous state with whole sections of brickwork broken away. On 20 December 1912 the buck was rigged up to a team of horses which succeeded in pulling the windmill to its destruction. The following January the event was mentioned in *The Miller* which stated that the mill '... one of the landmarks of Northamptonshire, has been taken down.' Some years later on 27

A view of Byfield mill taken from an old postcard. [Photo: Janet Blake]

Frank C. Gill's drawing of Byfield in 1899. [Reproduced with permission of R.C. Gill]

Byfield, October 1908

John Henry Bromley in 1908, aged 70. [Photo: Janet Blake]

October 1916, John Henry Bromley died at his home at Church House, Byfield. He was aged 79.

Some reminders of the post mill are still to be found. A book by the Reverend Poole chronicling the history of the village featured an illustration of the mill drawn by Frank C. Gill in 1899. The same picture appeared in Gill's article 'The Vanishing Windmill', published by the *Northampton County Magazine* in 1928. Recently three millstones were unearthed at the site and they are now in the possession of a local builder. Although time and time again the field has been ploughed over, a crop mark of the windmill is said still to exist.

CLIPSTON POST MILL

Clipston lies three and a half miles south of Market Harborough, and many years ago was host to one of the county's most famous landmarks. Along the narrow, hilly, gated road to Marston Trussell one would have found an excellent example of a Northamptonshire post mill complete with single storey roundhouse, horizontally boarded buck and four clockwise common sails. It was always a favourite meeting place for villagers who would watch the gathering of the Pytchley Hunt which used the windmill as an assembly point. From the mill itself one was treated to a splendid view of the surrounding countryside. Indeed, from this location it was claimed that on a clear day one could see Leicester.

Clipston mill could be seen from the London and North-western Railway, making it something of a landmark and the pride of the villagers. It is said that visitors to the village would be subjected to a tour of the site before setting foot in Clipston, and it was to be such attention that would indirectly cause its destruction.

Depicted on the Eyre and Jefferys county map of 1779 and Bryant's 1824 edition as 'Clipstone Windmill' it was curiously absent from Greenwood's map of the same period. The slightly later directory entries reveal that the windmill was owned and run by the venerable Buswell family, who dominated many of the local trades through Clipston. Buswells ran the local post office, the local public house ('The Red Lion'), and were farmers, shoemakers and butchers. Ephraim Buswell served as a plumber and glazier, while Nathaniel Buswell, a baker in 1861, was listed eight years later as a tax collector!

Six bakeries stood within the village, all seemingly dependent on the flour supplied by miller Thomas Buswell during the 1840s. Melvill's directory implied that by this time Thomas Buswell, jun., had succeeded his father as miller, and was also engaged in running one of the bakeries. By 1874 Mrs Charles Buswell (probably Thomas junior's widow) was dutifully conducting the business along with her son John, who eventually took over between 1885 and 1890. Like the rest of the family, John Buswell was a religious man who disliked working on a Sunday. His home was next door to the chapel where many of his relatives lay buried. John had cause to be grateful to God for the many years of prosperity brought to him by the mill, providing plentiful supplies for retailers in other districts as well as the village's six bakeries.

Sadly, though, Clipston post mill's success was short-lived, as other more efficient methods of corn milling became widespread. Overshadowed by the larger concerns, grinding at Clipston mill came to a halt around 1900.

Although idle, the wooden structure remained in a good state of repair, and no doubt continued to draw attention from local people, including children. Regular visitors included the sons of solicitor Mr W. Wartnaby, who lived at Clipston House. In the spirit of adventure, or mischief, his children would delight in climbing the sails, much to the disapproval of John Buswell who was able to watch their activities from his home. Angered by the boys' disregard for his property he threatened to have the

Clipston post mill from an old postcard. The original photograph is held by Mr M.D. Wilford. [Photo: A.C. Smith]

mill pulled down, but to no avail. On the next occasion the pranksters succeeded in bringing the mill into wind, allowing the sails to revolve. Enraged by this, Mr Buswell carried out his threat, and in 1903 the mill was demolished.

This contrasts sharply with the report of events in the March 1909 edition (vol. 3, no. 17) of *Northants Notes and Queries* which states that the mill was sold to a Mr T. Hickson of Market Harborough, who immediately having bought it had it dismantled, and by April 1906 only 'a heap of rubbish' remained.

The empty site was purchased by the Oxendon Rural District Council, later merged with Brixworth Council which was noteworthy for converting the site into a refuse tip. Thankfully the dump is today no more, and the area has reverted back to farmland once again. John Buswell never lived to see this as he died some time between the wars. His grandson, who still lives in Clipston, is the last of the family line.

This information, along with much more was supplied by 83-year-old Mr M. D. Wilford of Clipston.

COTTINGHAM TOWER MILL

Cottingham is situated between Corby and Market Harborough and is best approached by the A427 near the Great Oakley crossroads. It is a peaceful village set amid hilly countryside. The skyline is dominated by the steeple of the parish church. To the north-east, in an area once known as the meadows, stand the remains of a tower mill. In the summer of 1987 the mill comprised three storeys surrounded by scaffolding. Two and a half floors are of limestone and ironstone. The second storey had been repaired and heightened. This consisted of a red brick inner wall built onto the original stonework. The ground at the base of the structure had been cleared away exposing the stone foundations which extended out from the tower. A recent visit revealed the conversion now complete, with its tiled cone roof and built-on large semi-circular extension in matching stone. Although there is still an amount of waste ground in the vicinity, the area generally has been built up in recent years, and many houses now form the Millfield estate, with the conversion located in Windmill Close.

In its working days the tower mill stood upon a mound. It was four storeys high and powered by four anti-clockwise sails. This mill never carried a fantail, and had to be brought into wind with the aid of a luffing wheel and an endless chain. Windows did not feature at the top floor level, but at other levels they were set one above the other rather than in a spiral fashion. This particular tower mill displays a very distinct batter (taper) and is said to have been heightened during its life. If so, this would

A detail of Cottingham tower mill from the drawing in the porchway of St Mary Magdalene Church in Cottingham.

51

Cottingham mill photographed by Nigel Moon in 1963.

account for the lack of windows at the dust floor. Some floors within the mill were very high, especially the second. Two pairs of stones were mounted upon the first floor which was supported by posts from the ground. At the stone floor an iron lever had been installed for raising the millstones. These are assumed to have been overdriven. The only indication of this is that the upright shaft is said to have been positioned above the millstones. The shaft itself was assembled from two halves of wood probably clamped together with iron bands. All the machinery was of wooden construction, and it is claimed very little metal could be found internally.

Unfortunately, the date of the windmill's erection is unknown. It is absent on the county map of 1779 but can be seen on the Ordnance Survey map of 1825. During the latter part of the mill's life it was owned and worked by Mr George Atkins. (In his *Notes on Northamptonshire Windmills*, Herbert E. S. Simmons refers to him as Adkins, but the trade directories show Atkins).

Much of the following information was recalled by 94-year-old Mr Arthur Claypole of Middleton in 1981.

Together with his wife, Mr Atkins inhabited one of four cottages situated up a hill half a mile from the tower mill near the village school. Two of the cottages were demolished in later years, and the other two were modified to make a single home long after George Atkins's death just after the turn of the century. The couple never had any children and, although the miller worked hard, Cottingham tower mill was never very profitable. As Mr Claypole stated 'George Atkins was never a rich man'. Also remembered was the mill itself. 'It had four sails, a round dome top and cords for bringing the top part round into the wind.'

One Sunday night in 1894 or 1895 a violent storm hit the village. High winds damaged many houses, and trees were blown down, some across roads. In an effort to save his mill, Mr Atkins had luffed it round to face the wind. Sadly, his action did not prevent the cap and sails being torn from the tower. In the event the upper structure received much damage. Possibly due to economics, no repairs were undertaken and the mill was roofed over and subsequently used as a store. A local blacksmith, Mr

The broken stump at Cottingham as seen in 1980.

Cottingham during rebuilding in August 1987.

In April 1990 conversion work was still in progress.
[Photo: The author]

The spacious extension overwhelms the windmill tower which some years ago was almost demolished. [Photo: The author]

Swinger, obtained the property in the 1900s, and it later passed to a Mr Jarvis.

During 1935, windmill artist Karl S. Wood depicted Cottingham mill as a four floor tower with damaged walls about the curb. Two years later it was bought by a Mr Carter who proposed to turn the mill into a water tower by installing pumping equipment within a metal tank on top. A following inspection revealed the dust floor wall was badly cracked causing the curb to distort. Inside, the flooring was found to be in a ruinous and dangerous condition. Much of the stonework had crumbled away over the years. This was later repaired with cement rendering. All the wooden machinery was removed with the exception of one stone pair. The other set was taken by Mr Carter and set up as garden ornaments at his home, a newly built bungalow in Middleton. Unfortunately, Cottingham's pumping station proved unsuccessful in concept, and the idea was abandoned. As a last resort Mr Carter investigated the possibilities of converting the tower into a dwelling, but this plan was also dropped.

The tower remained derelict until the late 1950s or early 1960s when it was truncated to three storeys in height. A flat roof was added and its presumed use as a store continued by its then owner, Mr Lawson. Soon afterwards the stump and the surrounding land (at one time all allotments) were acquired by the Anglian Water

Authority. Not being fenced off, the mill inevitably became a target for vandals.

By the mid 1970s the whole site was under development. A new housing estate threatened the stump's future. A group of workmen took it upon themselves to start dismantling the remains, resulting in much damage to the second storey. The act caused an outcry amongst local people, and eventually the windmill was spared. In 1981 Cottingham tower mill had been fenced-in, forming part of a garden backing on to a house in Bancroft Road. Remains of the first and second floor beams could still be seen at that time.

Although no photographs of the working windmill have been found as yet, a sketch has been discovered in the parish church. In the porch of St Mary Magdalene, Cottingham, hangs a detailed nineteenth century drawing of the church. In the background the tower mill can be clearly defined. It is depicted with a boat or gable cap and four sails.

My thanks go to the Reverend Father, Geoffrey Ward, of St Mary's and to his Warden, Mr Ron Claypole, who was 72 in 1987. He is a distant relative of Arthur Claypole who died in 1986 aged 99.

EAST HADDON TOWER MILL

Seven miles north-west of Northampton and almost the same distance north-east of Daventry is the small village of East Haddon where some years ago stood one of the county's most attractive tower mills. This picturesque landmark was situated one mile west of the village, just off the Ravensthorpe road, and was built of locally made sandstone blocks, which Major C. A. Markham would later describe in his *Northants Notes and Queries* as giving the mill 'a warm and pleasing colour'. The tower stood three storeys high and was crowned with an unusual cap that could have been said to have been cone-shaped. Four clockwise sweeps — at least two of them were common sails — were brought into wind probably by a wheel and winch, but the headframe rearwards makes one wonder if at one time a fan cradle was fitted. To its curb the

East Haddon tower mill circa 1906. A few years later the sail stocks were removed and the cap dismantled. [Photo: Philip Davis]

East Haddon mill as it appeared in July 1937, showing its poll end and possibly the remains of a fan cradle. [Photo: H Meyer collection via A.C. Smith]

tower is believed to have been around 35 feet high, and the base diameter was 23 feet. There were two ground floor doorways opposite each other, 6 feet 6 inches in height and 3 feet 6 inches in width. The wall thickness at this level was about 2 feet.

East Haddon tower mill does not appear on Thomas Jefferys' map of 1779, but is marked on Bryant's 1824-26 county map. However, an earlier reference of 17 June 1820 in the *London Gazette* mentions a bankrupt John Wadsworth being forced to sell 'a substantial stone built windmill' within the parish of East Haddon. The report went on to say that the mill was in 'full trade' and would be sold together with newly erected house and stables then in the occupation of Mr Richard Jellis.

Early directory entries for East Haddon are sparse, but it is known that in 1847 the miller was farmer John Andrews, and by 1854 it had passed to James and Harding Andrew. Melvill's directory of 1861 also records James and Harding Andrew, and this appears to be the last entry, for in Kelly's trade directory of 1864 no millers are mentioned, and the only Andrew listed is William Andrew as a shopkeeper. Succeeding the Andrew family was Mr Dexter, the last miller at East Haddon. He operated the windmill for a number of years, during which time it became known locally as 'Old Dexter's Mill'. Around the 1870s or 1880s Mr Dexter ceased working the mill and left to become a builder. A Mr Robinson then bought the now derelict mill, which he is said to have owned for between forty and fifty years. A member of the East Haddon Parish Council, Mrs Dickens (82-years-old in 1980) remembered that Robinson was also the publican at the nearby 'Why Not Inn', later renamed the 'Buckby Lion'. According to Stanley Freese, Robinson died at the age of 95 some time before 1929. Also recorded was the fact that the mill was derelict when he was a boy!

Mrs Dickens was one of six children of Mr Baskott, assistant to Mr Brocas Clay, who had just purchased the Buckby Folly (a large country house near the 'Why Not Inn'), the windmill and the mill house. Mr Baskott took up residence in the mill house in 1906 by which time most of the tower mill's machinery had been removed. By this time the structure was in a sorry state with only the windshaft, and supposedly the brake wheel, contained within the framework of the conical cap. One pair of sail stocks remained intact until they were removed around 1910 by Mr Baskott who was no doubt concerned for the safety of his family. Some time later the cap collapsed, the remains of which were quickly dismantled, leaving the windshaft intact. Meanwhile, the derelict tower served as a cattle shelter, and a home for nesting pigeons.

In 1917 Brocas Clay died. Soon afterwards the Baskott family left the mill house. This was eventually purchased along with the mill and the Buckby Folly by Mr Phillips, a dealer in horses. Later, a Ravensthorpe builder, Mr Leatherland, bought the property, and gradually set about demolishing the tower between 1949 and 1950 to re-use the stone to build a wall at Thornby. Fortunately the foundations were spared and now serve as the border to a flower bed.

Although neglected and often overlooked, the derelict mill was not forgotten by enthusiasts and it featured in a number of publications. George Long in his book *The Mills of Man* published in 1931, described East Haddon windmill as 'a handsome typical tower mill', and a brief history of the mill can be found in the 1913 edition of the *Northamptonshire Notes and Queries* along with an illustration by Major C. A. Markham. A retouched photograph of the mill is to be seen in Richard Bennett and John Elton's *History of Corn Milling — Volume 2*, originally published in 1899. The photograph depicts the mill with its ruined cap and one set of stocks bearing a single clockwise common sail. Though the picture had been incorrectly captioned as 'Long Buckley, Hants' it is without doubt East Haddon.

In the Simmons *Notes on Northamptonshire Windmills*, G. N. Shann wrote of it in 1937 as a three floored 'roestone' tower with a shrub growing from the top of the structure 'giving it a rather ludicrous appearance'. A later drawing by Karl S. Wood executed in April 1939 displayed the building in a similar condition.

In a letter from the current owners of the site the author was fortunate to learn that the mill's remains were safe for the time being from any future plans. He was also informed of the sad death of Mrs Dickens.

EASTON-ON-THE-HILL TOWER MILL

Follow the A43 towards Stamford where, half a mile south of the North-amptonshire, Leicestershire and Lincolnshire county boundaries, you will pass through the village of Easton-on-the-Hill. Standing some 300 or 400 yards from the road, almost overwhelmed in foliage — a sign of years of abandonment — one can clearly see the shell of a tower mill. Easton mill is noted for being Northamptonshire's most northerly remaining windmill, an honour once bestowed on Glinton tower mill until the border changes of 1965 brought the Soke of Peterborough into amalgamation with Huntingdonshire, and later Cambridgeshire in 1974.

Access to the site presents some problems, but not enough to hinder those filled with the spirit of adventure, mostly children and windmill enthusiasts. The old original track boarded by a stone wall is now vastly overgrown, and following the path from a neighbouring field is the only option, taking care not to damage the crops. One is then faced with scrambling up a stone-filled mound, and only then is the tower mill truly visible. Although giving the appearance of a truncation, Easton mill remains at its full height of three storeys (evidence of this could be verified within by the apertures through which the curb retainers or anchor irons passed, visible in 1980 but covered by ivy when seen again in 1988.)

The tower is stone built with tar on top of cement rendering, much of which is flaking off and littering the site, as are many fallen stones. The best way of entering the structure is through the eastern doorway, but not before being confronted by a five foot drop to the basement floor. As one would expect, the building is totally empty. In 1963 it was visited by miller Nigel Moon, and he observed a solitary millstone in the basement, but by 1980 even that had gone. There are six window-ways, two within reach, measuring 3 feet by 3 feet 6 inches. Three doorways exist, two at 'mound floor' level are 6 feet 7 inches by 3 feet 10 inches, while the single basement doorway is 6 feet 8 inches by 3 feet 10 inches. The wall thickness at this point is 2 feet 10 inches and only 2 feet at 'mound floor' level. The last but nevertheless most important calculation was that of the base diameter which measures 22 feet.

During the nineteenth century the working mill would have made an inspiring sight, the black tower contrasting with its four white sails and gabled cap. Two of the sweeps were cloth-covered common sails, while the other two were shuttered, possibly spring sails. A tailpole comprising a single beam and braces was fixed to the cap and gave the mill an appearance similar to that of a Dutch windmill, but at the same time presented some problems with leverage. A simple solution adopted by many millers was to erect short posts around the windmill, then fit a winch to the tailpole. A chain would be played out and looped over a suitable stake. The miller would then wind the cap round to the post where the process would be repeated with the next stake until the sails were brought back into wind. It is known that this method was adopted at Easton mill, but sadly no trace of the posts remains.

Early references to the mill included windmill symbols on the 1824 Ordnance

A rare photograph of Easton mill during its active days. Behind the common and spring sails, the braces for the tailpole can be seen. This arrangement was typical of Dutch windmills. [Photo: S. L. Spademan]

Survey and the 1825-26 Greenwood map, and local history tells of a tragic event which took place on 8 March 1826 when a woman passing close by the working windmill received a blow to the head from one of the sails and died as a result. Miss Stancer was no more than 20 years of age when she met her death. Sadly, accidents of this kind were not uncommon. In 1845 57-year-old Mrs Sarah Northen was killed in much the same way by a windmill in the Kettering area. Millers, too, risked such mishaps when leaving their mills into the path of rotating sweeps, which is one reason why most windmills have two ground floor doorways providing workers with an alternative exit. At the time of Miss Stancer's demise the tower was being run by a Mr Dexter, and naturally it became known as 'Dexter's Mill', a tradition which continued long after his death in 1878.

This 1935 picture of Easton mill was taken from almost the same angle as that on page 59. By this time the mill was no more than a shell, and the track to the mill was inaccessible. [Photo: Donald W. Muggeridge]

Easton-on-the-Hill windmill was then taken over by Mr Sidney Spademan who employed three men, two to tend the horses and work the surrounding fields, and one as assistant miller. Around 1890 the mill passed to Ernest Spademan, Sidney having left to work at the tall tower mill at Kings Cliffe (see page 82), and subsequently by 1898 the watermill at Woodnewton, near Wansford. Ernest had left long before, and another member of the Spademan family, George, had taken charge. Obviously placing great faith in the tower mill's capabilities, George expanded the business by constructing a bakery. Under Sidney, the mill had supplied many of the surrounding villages with its produce, but the same success was not forthcoming for George Spademan, miller and baker. With the failure of the bakery the windmill ceased work. The 1906 Ordnance Survey map records Easton as an 'Old Windmill', perhaps emphasizing that at this time it was derelict.

About the time of the First World War the mill was gutted by a firm of millwrights. The sails would have been removed first, followed by the cap, then probably the internal machinery. Floorboards and all the principal beams were also taken out and, together with the rest of the gear, were sold off. The stones were reported to have been used to grind wheat and barley, indicating they were a mixture of French burrs and Derbyshire peaks. They, too, were included in the sale (with the exception of the single millstone seen by Nigel Moon). The end result was the empty shell that can be seen today.

A notable collection of enthusiasts have paid their respects to Easton mill during its years of decay, including Karl S. Wood in July 1932, and Stanley Freese two years later. In June 1935 Easton was pictured by Donald W. Muggeridge, and many years later the grand master of the Windmill Survey, Arthur C. Smith, photographed the mill in 1972. While probing around the site in 1980 the author and a friend stumbled across the foundations of the bakery, and a small building no more than 4 feet square. During my visit in August 1988 I was glad to note that little had changed. As I started to leave it began to rain. The north side of the tower soon became wet, giving the tarred surface a very glossy, clean finish, making this small empty tower still a proud memorial to a once fine mill.

My thanks go to Henry Wozniak and to the Reverend A. J. H. Francis of Easton Rectory for their assistance with this account.

Easton mill covered in foliage in 1980. Little has changed since that time.
[Photo: The author]

Finedon mill from a postcard dated 1910.

FINEDON TOWER MILL

The earliest reference to a windmill in Finedon occurs in a document dating from 1630, when it was said to share the parish with three watermills previously mentioned in the Domesday survey. The windmill, possibly a post mill, was depicted on the Eyre and Jefferys map of 1779, but within forty years it had vanished, only to be replaced by another windmill. The new mill, this time a tower mill, was built in 1818 on the same site as the former mill by a local squire, Sir John English Dolben. It is in what is now known as Station Road and originally formed part of the Westfield Lodge Estate. The tower was constructed of ironstone, and although its windmill features are not known, one thing is certain: the tower was furnished with a stage, because a ring of square holes in the wall can still be seen six feet from the ground.

The trade directories list Joseph Burr from Finedon Lodge as a miller and farmer, his name appearing in the 1847, 1854, 1864 and 1869 editions. Unfortunately, they fail to show whether he worked the windmill or one of the watermills. This is further complicated, as the family that currently inhabit the tower mill claim the alteration was carried out in 1845. However, there is no proof to reinforce the statement.

The windmill may have been damaged in a storm, which could account for its short life. The subsequent work of conversion was undertaken for Mr William Harcourt Isham Mackworth-Dolben, a Justice of the Peace who had formerly held the position of Sheriff of Northamptonshire. Finedon mill was only one of several buildings constructed or altered by Mackworth-Dolben between the 1840s and late 1850s. He chose to re-create the Gothic style in his works, all of which bear his initials. Finedon mill has often been described as a folly. Indeed, with its castellated, decorative additions and its proximity to the ill-fated Volta Tower (a true folly) it is understandable, though incorrect. The carvings can still be seen, and are truly remarkable. On the eastern side of the tower at the level of the first floor is set one of the millstones (in this case a peak stone). Upon it are cast the letters: R.E.S.T., and above is fixed a stone scroll displaying: EXMILL COTTAGE, the name given to the converted windmill by Mr Mackworth-Dolben. Still on the eastern side, below the third floor window, are two stone shields bearing the initials: W.H.I. and M.D. The windows at the third floor are based on the mock gothic design, and to the right of the eastern window is a tablet marked with the date 1818, in celebration of the tower's erection.

Exmill Cottage remained in the possession of Mr Mackworth-Dolben for many years. In 1871 it was occupied by his gamekeeper, Richard Turner, who lived there with his family. Ownership of the property passed to William's daughter, Ellen Frances Julia Mackworth-Dolben, who lived until February 1912. The following June the converted windmill was put up for sale by auction, together with the Volta Tower and the rest of her estate. It was the end of an era, perhaps signified by damage received by the tower in 1914 when the castle parapet partly collapsed. Smaller battlements were rebuilt soon afterwards, and it is only when old and new photo-

Finedon tower conversion today, showing the large extension on the right, modified in the 1960s.
[Photo: The author]

graphs of the structure are compared that any major difference can be detected. Repairs of that kind could not be applied to the near-by Volta Tower which suddenly collapsed in 1951.

Between the wars one Mr Lennard rented much of the surrounding land which later passed to his daughter, Mrs Brown. For four years, from 1956 until 1960, Mr Bill Southam rented the property. In 1963 Exmill Cottage was purchased by the present owners who, after an inspection discovered that the conversion was in need of extensive repair. The two extensions were rebuilt and the tower itself modernized. Many floorboards and beams were replaced, but one which clearly dates from the windmill's working days still supports the first floor of the tower, and is exposed in the ground floor lounge's ceiling. Although a busy farmer, the owner has spent much time re-pointing and cleaning the stonework, and was only too pleased to answer my questions during my visit in 1980.

My notes and measurements reveal that the four storey mill has a base diameter of 25 feet, with a thickness at the ground floor wall of almost three feet, and at the top of the tower two feet. Access onto the roof is possible, offering a fine view, and while enjoying the scene I was reminded of a very similar conversion that once existed at Kneesworth in Cambridgeshire. It was much smaller than the mill at Finedon, standing a mere three storeys in height, and was also rebuilt in mock Gothic style, but has since been demolished.

GREENS NORTON TOWER MILL

Greens Norton tower mill had the dubious honour of being the last windmill to be deliberately felled within the county at a time when the Northamptonshire windmill was already a 'threatened species'. Prior to its destruction the tower mill had stood four storeys in height and gave the appearance of a red brick construction. Upon entering, however, one would have immediately noticed the internal wall of white painted stone. With most of the machinery missing and the cap totally disintegrated it was a far cry from its working days. Decades before, the mill had operated with four patent sails taking power to two stone sets, the whole thing topped with a dome-shaped cap.

Built during the early part of the nineteenth century, the tower mill, known as 'Norton mill', worked in conjunction with two watermills. One of them, known as 'Kingthorn mill', was situated south-west of the windmill, and the other — confusingly also named 'Norton mill' — stood south-east of the tower mill. All three featured on Bryant's county map of 1824-26; the windmill with the standard 'post mill' symbol, and Kingthorn and Norton mills each captioned 'watermill'. Similar detail was applied to the Ordnance Survey map of 1834 which labelled both the windmill and the south-eastern watermill as 'Norton Mill'.

Early directory references date from 1840 when Thomas Grisbrook was the miller. By 1847 millers in the parish included Mr J. A. Johnson and Mr George Stops, who is known to have owned both the tower mill and Kingthorn watermill for many years. Unfortunately, the directories fail to acknowledge individual millers and assistants to Mr Stops, but Mr W. Foxley was listed at Greens Norton in the 1869 edition and Mr T. Gallard in Kelly's 1877 volume. John Fawcett Stops (possibly George's son) was grinding grain at Kingthorn, as was another family member, William Stops, who from the mills in his charge during the 1870s, seemed to have enjoyed his work. These included Stoke Bruerne tower mill, Twickets watermill at Heathcote, near Towcester, and (according to the 1877 directory) a third mill at Towcester.

In 1883 George Stops died, and in December of that year Kingthorn mill and the windmill were put up for auction. A second auction was held in February 1884 in which Kingthorn mill was described as a 'water and steam corn mill working four pairs of stones'. The windmill, which was Lot 2, was listed as 'a powerful tower mill with four patents driving two pairs of stones'. The buyer may have been Mr Albert Lawrence, who thereafter for a short while continued to work the mills.

Milling by wind came to an end at Greens Norton just after the turn of the century, and the idle tower mill was purchased in 1914 by Mr Albert Booth who intended to use the building, along with some neighbouring sheds, as carpentry workshops. The mills large ground floor doorway made it ideal for this type of work. Mr Booth's daughter, Mrs Mary Furniss, recalled that her father tackled various kinds of woodwork, including wheelwrighting and coffin making. After the First World War Mr Booth had the four sails taken down as they were in a dangerous condition. This

Greens Norton tower mill circa 1930. The cap clearly shows signs of deterioration, although the building was being used as a workshop. [Photo: Mary Furniss]

would also have been about the time that the windshaft, brake wheel and possibly other pieces of machinery were removed, but the cap and headframe were left in place.

The windmill field (now Bradden Way) was rented by a Major Williams for the training and 'breaking' of horses, and to calm the animals a young Mary Booth would delight in playing an organ which had been installed in the mill.

It is clear that most of the carpentry work had been carried out on the ground floor. The other levels were left to time and the elements, and it was in this condition that the tower mill was seen by Stanley Freese in 1934. Mr Freese described the mill as a derelict brick tower with a 'slate dome' cap and no sails.

Five years later Karl S. Wood revealed in his drawing of the mill a considerable amount of deterioration to the cap which had partly collapsed within the building. Undaunted by these problems Albert Booth, together with his two sons, continued with the carpentry business until his death in 1965. After that no further work was undertaken and the mill eventually passed to Albert's youngest son.

By 1972 the tower was truly derelict, with the cap gone and the surrounding land

The mill a year before it was demolished in 1973.
[Photo: Nigel Moon]

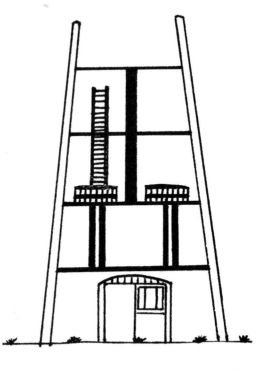

A cutaway sketch of Greens Norton in 1972,
showing the first floor with its four posts
supporting two stone pairs. The upright shaft
supports the top floor.

overgrown. In September that same year enthusiast Nigel Moon explored the site in an effort to analyse the remnants of the windmill's machinery. The ground floor proved to be of little interest, but upon the first floor a loading door was evident, and one stone spindle and part of the tentering gear remained. Four wooden upright posts supported the second floor where the stones were situated. The two pairs of peaks were still contained within their timber vats, but apart from the wooden upright shaft little else was to be seen. Nigel concluded that the stones were overdriven, as the upright shaft terminated on the stone floor rather than passing through it, thereby disallowing the possibility of an underdrift great spur wheel. The top of the shaft had been cut off level with the underside of the dust floor which now served as the roof. Almost all the steps were missing, and in their place a rickety ladder set up on top of one of the stone vats ascended to the upper floors, themselves in an unsafe condition.

In 1973 the site which included one acre of land was sold, and the tower mill and the miller's house were demolished. A new housing estate was built upon the land. The site of the mill is now number 17 Bradden Way, according to Mrs Furniss.

HELLIDON TOWER MILL

For the occupiers of the converted tower mill at Hellidon, the building will always be regarded as a triumph, a monument to hard work and ambition, allowing them to escape from the rat race and set up home in an attractive dwelling situated in peaceful surroundings — a complete contrast to the rush of city life. No-one should feel anything but admiration for the determination of the family who made great personal sacrifices and suffered many a sleepless night to create their dream house from the ruined mill. Such an achievement should be applauded, but for a few the Hellidon story is tinged with sadness, for it is more than the tale of a ruin becoming a home. It is the memory of the county's last restorable windmill being lost forever with all its machinery.

The tower mill was constructed in 1842 (according to a plaque found within the mill) to replace an earlier one, possibly a post mill, that had stood on more or less the same site. Evidence of a mill at Hellidon could be traced back to 1642 when William Benson, the miller of Hellidon was recorded in the Southam Register of Burials. The windmill itself was depicted on various maps, including the 1779, 1825/26 and 1834

Hellidon tower mill early this century. Despite the loss of the fantail, the mill seems in good order.
[Photo: Maurice and Joyce Palmer]

By June 1936 the sails of Hellidon mill had decayed to an alarming extent. The mill was to remain derelict for the next 39 years. [Photo: Donald W. Muggeridge]

editions frequently referred to in this book. Its successor was built of red brick, three storeys in height and topped with an iron-sheeted dome cap. The sails were made up of four clockwise common sweeps brought into wind by a fantail. It was said that Hellidon mill was very powerful (probably due to its advantageous position on the summit of 'Windmill Hill') and was able to power no less than four pairs of stones.

Most of the machinery was of wooden construction including the windshaft to which was attached a cast-iron poll end. The shaft itself is said to have had a diameter of 18 inches tapering to 14 inches at its tail end. A clasp-arm brake wheel (with an iron brake) was fitted to the shaft and engaged a wooden wallower, also of clasp-arm construction, seated on a four-sided timber upright shaft measuring 13 1/2 inches square. This was connected to a clasp-arm great spur wheel with a 6 foot 6 inch diameter, and drove the four 18 inch diameter stone nuts, themselves fixed to square iron spindles. At the hub of the great spur wheel a toothed 'drum' (as described by G. N. Shann in 1937) probably took power to a wire machine suspended from the ground floor ceiling.

Of the stones themselves set upon the first floor of the mill, the northern and southern pairs had a diameter of 4 feet 6 inches, while the eastern set was just 4 feet and the western stones measured just 3 feet 8 inches. With all this tremendous weight the first floor had to be supported by two upright wooden posts, obviously allowing

Hellidon tower mill drawn in 1947 by Frank C. Gill. [Reproduced with the permission of R. C. Gill]

clearance for the underdriven machinery (including a single master governor). During a conversation about this mill with Nigel Moon, one of the country's few remaining windmillers, Nigel expressed his astonishment at the number of stone pairs in such a small mill. He believed it would have been unlikely for all four pairs to have worked at the same time, and it was feasible that one set may have been kept in a state of constant standby. Dressing the stones must have presented its problems. The mill was very cramped inside, especially the stone floor, which did not even offer a proper passageway, and as a result the miller would continually have to scramble over the assemblies to carry out his duties.

Most unusual was the fact that all four pairs were French burrs instead of the normal mixture of burrs and peaks. In later years during a period of 'great calm' a steam engine was brought in to assist the idle windmill, and an aperture was made just above the eastern ground floor window to accept a metal drive shaft powered from an external pulley. At the end of the $2\frac{1}{2}$ inch square shaft an iron cog 12 inches in diameter engaged the underside of the great spur wheel, while fixed to the other end of the axle, near the wall, a 3 foot 4 inch diameter gear is believed to have powered an adjacent dresser.

Mr Moon reminded the author that although the steam engine drove the stones via the great spur wheel, it is doubtful that an average portable engine (no evidence of an engine shed was found) of between 6 H.P. and 8 H.P. could have tackled more than one or two stone sets at one time.

Throughout its working life the tower mill was run by the Gilks family. One of the first, Mr Edward Gilks, was listed in Kelly's Trade Directory of 1847 as a farmer and miller. His name could also be found in the Electoral Register of 1836 which recorded him as having 'freehold house and land in his own occupation'. By 1854 Edward had been chronicled in that year's directory as a baker, in addition to his other trades.

Melvill's edition of 1861 revealed that the farm, mill and bakery were operating, with Mrs Ann Gilks in charge, and continued to do so until some time after 1884. By that time Edward Aris Gilks (possibly junior?) was also working on the farm, and Miss Margaret Gilks was a dressmaker by trade. The windmill passed to Edward around 1890, while Mrs Gilks continued to run the farm. The last entry in the directories recording the windmill at work could be found in the 1903 volume. In the main body of the book, in the Hellidon section, Ann Gilks was listed as a farmer, while Edward Aris continued grinding corn at the mill. However, one must assume, if the directories are correct, that it was sometime between 1903 and 1906 that the tower mill stopped work, for within the pages of the 1906 edition Edward is documented as a farmer only. This was repeated in the 1910 manual which was notable in revealing another member of the Gilks family — George, then a farmer. Only he, along with Margaret Gilks, the dressmaker, were mentioned in the 1914 directory, but by then Hellidon mill was already derelict.

During the years of abandonment one of the first casualties of neglect was the fantail, which was lost or removed before the mid-1930s. A postcard circa 1933 showed the mill minus the fan, but otherwise in seemingly good order, including the four common sweeps. It is therefore surprising that none other than Stanley Freese could have wrongly identified them. On page 151 of his book *In Search of English Windmills* (1931) he wrote: '...[Hellidon] has two cloth sails and two shuttered, and is similar in this respect to Tansor mill, near Oundle ...' Freese redeemed himself by reminding us that this mill, together with others at Twyford, Sulgrave and Woodhouse Eaves, was visible from the Great Central railway line. A somewhat more detailed study was made by Donald Muggeridge, who photographed the derelict mill in June 1936 when it was still in a reasonable state, although some damage to the sails was evident.

It was G. N. Shann who, after an inspection carried out in 1937, claimed that a wooden 'Y' wheel contributed to winding the mill. Traces of this were said to be visible, but close examination of Mr Muggeridge's photographs fail to reveal anything. The 'Y' wheel theory was not pursued by Herbert E. S. Simmons during his visit of April 1944, but he commented upon the well-preserved state of the machinery as Shann had done. In his notes Simmons recalled that one of the sails had broken off at the poll end and could be found near the base of the tower. The metal sheets, fitted many years previously to the upper external walls in an attempt to give some protection to the brickwork, were rusted and added to the mill's already forlorn appearance.

Inside, Simmons noticed a wooden curb still in place, as were the six centering wheels responsible for rotating the cap. By this time the ladder to the second floor was missing, preventing a thorough inspection, but Mr Simmons managed to obtain much information.

Also mentioned in his notes were the deserted out-buildings located east of the mill, including stables and some sheds. A few yards to the tower's southern side there was an old coach house, also derelict, and itself destined to be converted.

After the destruction of Northamptonshire's last surviving post mill at Bozeat (see page 36), five tower mills remained within the county with some remnants of their machinery, including Barnack, Eye, Greens Norton, Hellidon and Werrington (the latter still working by auxiliary power). No moves were made in the direction of preservation, and by 1953 the long awaited answer came from a spokesman on behalf of the Planning Department. Quite simply there was no money to spare and the County Council felt there was nothing worth restoring. Obviously the authorities were unaware of Hellidon's significance. Although in a ruined state it was by then the only windmill within the whole of the county (with the exception of Barnack in the Soke of Peterborough) with not only its machinery but also its cap, windshaft and sails. Even if restoration had been merely considered for a possible future project it would not have been too late. Ellis's mill in Lincoln, a tower mill completely rebuilt

Hellidon mill in 1971.
[Photo: Maurice and Joyce Palmer]

The auxiliary drive to a pair of millstones via the great spur wheel. [Photo: Nigel Moon]

from a burnt-out shell in 1977, was to prove that in years to come.

There was a brief period of hope in the first few weeks of 1967 when a bid was made to Daventry Rural Council by members of the Northamptonshire County Council to save what was then recognized as the last of its type. It was estimated the work would cost in the region of £4,300, and it was hoped some of the money would be forthcoming from grants under the Local Authorities (Historic Buildings) Act. On 7 February 1967 Daventry Rural Council agreed in principle to support the scheme, but the general feeling was that the problem should have been dealt with much earlier.

Exactly one year later Daventry Council accepted a recommendation from its Planning Committee to allow Hellidon tower mill to be converted into a dwelling. In the meantime it was deteriorating rapidly. Author and historian Mr Maurice Palmer photographed the mill in 1971 including the inside, which revealed most of the machinery in place, but ladders, floorboards and parts of the cap were missing. This was corroborated by Nigel Moon's colour slides taken a year later, which illustrated the extent of damage to the building. The cap had partly collapsed as had the fan cradle, although it remained roughly in position, and one of the stone pairs had broken free and was perched precariously above a doorway.

On 3 March 1975 a report appeared in *The Chronicle & Echo* giving details of the proposed plans of building company director, Mr Richard Hayward, who intended to convert only the ground floor of the tower, leaving the remaining gear in place and replacing the sails, so retaining its outward appearance. The 35-year-old Napton man expected to spend £30,000 on the project which included the construction of living quarters nearby. It is regretable that the scheme never materialized, and even more

The interior of Hellidon mill as seen from the ground floor in 1971. Most of the floorboards have gone, as have the ladders. The square upright shaft and the wallower can be clearly seen. [Photo: Maurice and Joyce Palmer]

unfortunate that the door to conversion had been forced open.

That same year the remains were purchased by a London couple, John and Carol Hitchcock, who '... gave up the fast jet-setting life of London ... to go and live off the land ...' as *The Chronicle & Echo* reported at the time. To obtain the windmill Mr Hitchcock had to give up his garage business, while his wife ended her career as a personnel manager with the Playboy Club. Both had to sell their sports cars and live in a caravan while the modifications to the tower mill were carried out. Within weeks all the machinery and stones had been removed, much of it left on the site, its future uncertain. It was around this time that Henry Wozniak of Wellingborough photographed the remains, and from his pictures later built up a series of detailed drawings of parts of the machinery.

The alterations to Hellidon mill had proved costly, but they were skilfully done, especially to the tower itself which was not only renovated but had a single storey extension built onto its eastern side. The ruined cap had been replaced by a shining dome roof of aluminium which contrasted sharply with the black painted tower.

About £40,000 was spent on creating a habitable interior including an entrance hall,

Hellidon mill as it is today. [Photo: The author]

bedroom and bathroom on the 16 foot diameter ground floor. Open tread steps lead to the first floor with a diameter of 15 feet 6 inches, this being the kitchen and dining room. At this point one should remember that all the rooms are essentially round, and fittings such as cupboards, radiators and the staircase had to be made specially curved to fit. A living room or lounge is situated on the second floor, and from here the loft, beneath the dome, can be reached by means of a pull-down ladder.

When not in the house the Hitchcocks could be found working in their vegetable garden or tending a small number of farm animals. Mr Hitchcock later branched out into market trading, while his wife attended St Crispin Hospital on a part-time basis as a psychologist.

After six years of this simple lifestyle the couple sold up and moved abroad. Soon afterwards Hellidon mill was purchased by another London family who used it as a weekend retreat, but the busy working lifestyle prevented any serious commitment, and within a short while the converted mill was back on the market. This was in 1984 and the price was £138,000. The sales brochure explained that the tower had received treatment against rising damp, and that the coach-house had recently been altered into a two storey dwelling. It was also pointed out that plans were afoot to link the cream-painted tower to the coach-house, making one large dwelling. Before that the previous occupant had planned to add two wings to the mill, then demolish the redundant coach-house, but fortunately this never happened.

It is said one can see four counties from the tower, now well established as a fine home. But, parts of the mill, such as the decaying wooden machinery, set up as garden ornaments, will always serve as a sad reminder of what could have been the only fully restored windmill in the whole of Northamptonshire.

KETTERING POST MILL

The Kettering post mill that survived into the first few months of this century is believed to have succeeded an earlier one mentioned in a grant from King James I in May 1609. Also included was a watermill and an animal-powered mill (namely a horse mill) which in time passed to the Duke of Montagu. An old map of Kettering dated 1782 included a windmill roughly at the same location later illustrated on the Eyre and Jefferys map of 1779 which curiously showed a second windmill in close proximity. Only one of them seems to have survived into the nineteenth century when it was the subject of an enclosure claim awarded to Abraham Mee in 1804. Greenwood's map of 1825/26 failed to include the windmill, but it was represented together with the watermill and a second windmill situated near the Uppingham (later Rockingham) road (now the A6003) upon the 1835 Ordnance Survey map. With the aid of another map, this time A. Bryant's plan of the county made between 1824 and 1826, one can identify the L-shaped lane that led past the post mill and eventually ended at the watermill as the much altered Windmill Avenue and Deeble Road.

Kettering windmill typified the kind of post mill found throughout the county during the last century with its horizontally boarded buck and single storey round-

Kettering post mill at the turn of the century, with the mill house. [Photo: F. Davison DCM]

A sketch of the 'Weekley Road Mill', showing the three diagonally positioned dormers.

house. Photographs taken during its final years portray the mill as a very simple construction, its rustic appearance enhanced by its battered and much repaired buck. One aspect of the mill's body worth mentioning is the very unusual addition of three diagonally positioned dormers on the right side facing the mill's breast. They may have been window ways, but their exact purpose is not known. Within the mill it is known that wooden clasp-arm brake and tail wheels, fixed to a wooden windshaft, took power via stone nuts to two pairs of stones, one set being French burrs. Also evident in the photographs is the absence of two of an original four clockwise sails, the loss of which occurred during a thunderstorm when the miller applied the brake rather too sharply causing one of the sweeps to snap off. Unable or unwilling to repair the damage, the miller removed the opposite sail and was seemingly content to run the windmill with only its remaining two sweeps.

This would have been about the time the mill was leased by the Coleman family who also rented the Rockingham Road tower mill which was built in 1821 to replace a post mill by Mr William Cunnington, a Kettering carpenter. It stood three storeys high and was crowned by a boat-shaped cap. Its clockwise sails, which consisted of two common and two patent sweeps, were winded by a tailpole and winch. The tower mill was later purchased by Cunnington's niece and sold to a Rothwell farmer, William Chater (or Charter in the directories) who ran it together with a bakery until 1858 when the premises passed to his son, also William.

Pigot's directory of 1830 recorded Daniel Hughes working at the post mill, sometimes referred to as the 'Weekley Road mill', while the nearby watermill or

The 'Rockingham Road' tower mill around 1890. This mill was also owned by the Coleman family. [Photo: F.A. Moore]

'Kettering mill' (so described on the 1834 Ordnance Survey map) was being run by Mr John Tingle. By 1840 Mr Tingle had taken over the post mill, but shortly afterwards moved into another dimension of the business. Mrs Jane Tingle was already established as a corn and flour dealer during the mid-1840s, and by 1861 John was following a similar trade according to Melvill's directory for that year. A deed dated 1853, now in the possession of Kettering historian Mr F. A. Moore (to whose assistance with this account I am indebted) shows the windmill was owned by Thomas Henry Gotch who leased it on a yearly basis for £25. One of the tenants may have been Thomas Miller whose name appears in the 1854 directory, although it is possible he was employed at the watermill, as Weekley Road was not mentioned. Also listed in the pages of another directory, this time Slater's of 1862, is John Bell, but it is unclear at which of the Kettering mills he worked. An earlier entry in an 1854 edition reveals that the tower mill was being operated by Samuel Allen of Uppingham Road. By 1861 he had been replaced by the venerable Colemans who are said to have run both the post and tower mills over a period of three generations — William Coleman senior at the post mill and his son, William junior at the tower. The 1861 directory is notable for its use of 'Rockingham Road' instead of the previous 'Uppingham Road'.

A reference should be made to John and Thomas Wallis, 'chicory and mustard millers' who were conducting business in the western part of the town at Newland

The ruins of Kettering post mill in 1900. Visible is the windshaft with its brake and tail wheels. The man is sitting on the main post. [Photo: F.A. Moore]

Street and nearby Tanners Lane during the mid to late nineteenth century. They probably owned a steam-driven mill (but this is no more than an educated guess). What is known is that by 1877 their operations had extended to Burton Latimer.

Weekley Road mill featured in the 1874 and 1876 trade manuals in which William Coleman was chronicled as the miller. By 1885, however, he seems to have moved on to Great Oxendon mill near Market Harborough, and one is left with the assumption that by this time the post mill had closed down.

The end was also drawing near for the Rockingham Road mill, for in 1891 the land near the mill was sold by William Chater the younger to the local authorities who built a school near the site. A builder, Mr Alfred Barlow, later obtained the remainder of the property, including the tower mill in 1894, and had it demolished to make way for houses.

Kettering post mill in its delapidated condition defied abandonment and the weather, and managed to remain standing into the twentieth century, but by May 1900 demolition work began on the derelict building. On 17 May (Mafeking Day) the half-dismantled ruin collapsed and was completely destroyed. The mill house survived, but it too was knocked down for a housing estate in 1962. Thankfully the planners incorporated some memorials into the development in the shape of Windmill Avenue, Windmill Walk and Mill Dale Road.

KINGS CLIFFE TOWER MILL

On 4 June 1818 an advertisement appeared in *The Stamford Mercury* calling for millwrights willing to help in the construction of a new tower windmill within the parish of Kings Cliffe. Those interested were to apply to 41-year-old Mr William Cunnington, who was to later organize the building of a brewery and maltings in the village. Work on the mill was scheduled to be finished within one year and three months, and the site chosen for the project was in West Street, almost in the centre of the village.

When completed the tower mill stood six storeys high with a decorative stage at its second floor. An ogee cap topped the structure, and an eight-bladed fantail auto-

Kings Cliffe tower mill in all its glory. [Photo: Courtesy County Record Office]

An attractive study of the tower mill some time after it ceased work.
[Photo: F.A. Moore]

matically brought the four sails round to face the correct wind direction. According to the original advertisement, the sail arrangement would comprise two patent sweeps (or as was stated 'two made upon Cubbitt's plan') and two commons able to carry eight yards of cloth. These were later replaced by four single shuttered anti-clockwise patent sails which took power, via an iron windshaft and a brake wheel with a diameter of nine feet, to three sets of stones. Two of the stone pairs were French burrs, with diameters of 4 feet 2 inches, while the third set consisted of two peak stones measuring 5 feet. Internally it is claimed the base was 20 feet across. Taking into account the wall thickness (possibly two or even three feet) the external diameter may have measured up to 26 feet, although this is not known for sure. Altogether the new mill resembled a Lincolnshire tower mill, with the exception of the fan cradle which was not inclined as were its northern cousins.

Apart from its spectacular tower mill, Kings Cliffe possessed a watermill (which survives as a conversion owned in 1980 by the Reverend Canon P. J. M. Bryan, MA, who also helped with this short history of the windmill) and a smock mill which was eventually wrecked in a storm in 1860. Such was the force of the gale that large numbers of trees were brought down, yet the tower mill seems to have escaped any serious damage and continued working under the supervision of William Cunnington junior. Cunnington the younger had inherited the business after his father's death in

Two photographs taken from the Peterborough Advertiser *recording the mill's destruction on 29 October 1925. [Photo: Courtesy of* The Peterborough Advertiser*]*

1850 at the age of 73. As before, the mill was used mainly to produce flour for the village bakery. The trade directories for 1847 and 1854 also list Mr T. Jelley and Mr H. Jelley respectively as Kings Cliffe millers. Fortunately, in later years the directories would distinguish between wind, water and steam-powered mills. One can only assume the Jelley's were employed at one of the other two mills in the parish (possibly at the watermill in this case).

Two other native millers mentioned included a Mr Branston of Hall Yard (1864) and Mr T. Clark (1871). These may have been watermillers. The village also had its own millwright, Groom Worrow. No doubt he was kept busy, not just in Kings Cliffe, but also in the surrounding area. Meanwhile, William Cunnington was recorded as a 'miller and brewer' in the 1871 directory, but by 1874 Joseph Slingsby junior had taken over at the tower mill, and William Cunnington continued his work as the maltster. Mr Slingsby was later joined by Sidney Spademan, a veteran from the Easton-on-the-Hill tower mill (see page 60). Together with the running of the windmill, both men were bakers. Mr Cunnington was still listed as maltster as late as 1885, but this too passed to Joseph Slingsby soon afterwards. Assistant miller Sidney Spademan had moved on to work at the watermill at Woodnewton, near Wansford, by 1898. Meanwhile, Cliffe watermillers between 1874 and 1903 included Obed Clarke,

Lucas Wade and later Mr G. Smith about the turn of the century.

The last windmiller at Kings Cliffe was Mr John Thomas Featherstone, who followed in the footsteps of his predecessors by also occupying the bakery. In 1903 he was listed in the trade directory as the baker of Telegraph Street. The 1906 volume records him baking in West Street. That same year the mill was referred to as 'a fine windmill'. By 1910 it had stopped work permanently.

For many years the tower mill remained a picturesque landmark, even when derelict. It proved to be a popular meeting place for villagers. Virtually complete, with the exception of its fan and some missing sail shutters, the tower proved to be very sound even though it had never been tarred. It would later be described by *The Peterborough Advertiser* as 'a splendidly preserved specimen' and was said to be in 'excellent order'. However attractive it was, safety had to be taken into consideration, and in 1924 the patent sweeps were removed by millwright and ex-seaman Mr J. E. Elsam. It was about this time that the brewery and maltings were knocked down.

The following year the recent owners, Colonel Hodgkin and his wife, sold the mill to the Looms Salvage Company of Leicester for demolition. Apparently Mrs Hodgkin took an instant dislike to the tower and immediately made arrangements for its destruction. Many tried to persuade the lady otherwise, but nothing could save the windmill from the inevitable. Preparations took three weeks. Responsible for the work was Mr Elsam who had removed the sails the year before. Felling the tower involved a system used on large industrial chimneys, all machinery and stones having been extracted and the cap dismantled. Joists and floorboards were also removed and stacked on the ground floor, later to be drenched in oil. Three quarters of the base was knocked out, then floorbeams acting as props erected either side of the doorway. More debris was then added to the pyre, and feather gaps were hammered out of the bottom wall. By now a large crowd had gathered, with many spectators also on rooftops to witness the old mill's downfall. At 2.27 p.m. on 29 October 1925 Mr Elsam lit the fire, and within a short time the flames, aided by a strong draught, had reached almost to the top of the tower. The first crack in the structure appeared above the door, and within ten minutes of being fired the timber props gave way causing the inevitable collapse. The spectacle had been recorded by reporters and photographers from *The Peterborough Advertiser* who gave a long graphic description of the windmill's demise.

In addition to the local press were members of the Gaumont Film Company. Interestingly, as well as a standard camera, a second model was used specifically for slow motion filming. The company planned to use the footage in their regular news programme *The Gaumont Graphic*. (In 1980 Henry Wozniak of Wellingborough made an effort to trace the film. After much investigation he was informed that it had long since been lost. Thankfully *The Peterborough Evening Telegraph* kindly supplied a copy of the original *Advertiser* photographs which accompany this account.)

And so Kings Cliffe's last windmill vanished forever because of a lady's insistence. Had circumstances been different it might have quite easily survived to the present day. Of the few remains are a millstone, from the tower mill, which is set up as a garden ornament, and the crop mark of the smock mill which, when conditions are favourable, can be detected from the air.

Long Buckby post mill circa 1910. This view shows to advantage the 'cone-shaped' roundhouse and the narrow ladder. [Photo: Mrs Clifton]

LONG BUCKBY POST MILL

It is claimed that the post mill originally stood at Weston-on-the-Welland until it was purchased by Mr Robert Ashby in about 1780. The mill was subsequently dismantled and transported to Long Buckby where it was re-erected upon Hannah Hill, just over a mile east of the village. It is said that, at this spot, from the top of the mill, one was able to see five counties. The post mill itself could be seen from both the Grand Union Canal and the London to Birmingham railway, and in time it became a noted landmark.

Although no windmills were shown at Long Buckby or Weston-on-the-Welland on the 1779 county map, Bryant's 1824-26 edition clearly displayed the Hannah Hill mill (also believed to have been known as 'Lodge Lane mill' after the track that eventually led to Patford Bridge.) In those days it was an open trestle post mill, leaving the great 2 foot 6 inch square main post and its 20 foot crosstrees exposed. The white-painted buck was horizontally boarded and topped with a curved roof, said to consist of iron sheets. Beneath this, two pairs of stones were driven by wooden brake and tail wheels, the power coming from four clockwise common sails. Winding was carried out with a tailpole. To the right side of this a narrow ladder led to the doorway. In most cases, even post mills with a single doorway, there would be a wide set of steps with the tailpole passing through the centre.

A similar mill stood three quarters of a mile north, on the West Haddon road at Cotton End (see page 198). Another post mill is known to have been located much nearer Long Buckby to the south of East Street, and two watermills were situated at the western end of the village. 'Upper Mill' and 'Lower Mill' were being run by John Jellis and Robert Ashby until the latter's death in 1815. Robert's son George then took up the challenge and also assisted at one of the two remaining post mills at Hannah Hill or Cotton End. The miller at 'Lodge Lane' in 1830 was Richard Denny, who was responsible for the construction of the single storey roundhouse in about 1860. Unlike conventional roundhouses this example was tapered and was often described as a 'cone-shaped structure'. With no roof to protect the trestle from the elements a skirt was added beneath the buck, and during winding, as with Barnack post mill, the roundhouse roof would have been seen to move with the body. A narrow petticoat formed part of the skirt, and this has sometimes been mistaken for some sort of curb. As a result, Long Buckby post mill has been referred to as a composite mill; a kind of hybrid mill in which a post mill body was supported and traversed upon a short tower (few examples were built and none survive). This myth was exploded by Major C. M. Markham in his *Northants Notes and Queries* in August 1920. After describing the trestle, Markham wrote of the roundhouse: '... this of course was not necessary for the stability of the structure.'

In 1864, Vincent Frisby from Naseby was working at the windmill, and by 1874 Fred Muddiman had taken charge. It is known that Mr Muddiman also ran one of the watermills. The 'Lower Mill' was converted to steam power after 1881 when the

A later photograph than that on page 84, displaying damage to the roundhouse. Note that the tailpole is missing.
[Photo: Philip Davis]

Northampton to Rugby railway line cut through the river, thereby greatly reducing the supply of water to the mill. Between 1890 and 1894 William Henry Ashby junior, a cousin of George Ashby, had the honour of being Hannah Hill's last miller. Trade directories for the 1890s record that William was grinding with the aid of wind, steam and water power. By 1898 only steam and water were being used.

After it ceased work, the post mill seemed to deteriorate rapidly, and towards the end of its life the building was in a very ruinous condition. Only one of the common sails was left intact, with just the empty stock of its opposite remaining. The roundhouse also suffered much damage, the brickwork on one side holed and crumbling. On 2 January 1914 the then owner, Mr A. M. Allen, a farmer, had the mill demolished.

Few photographs of the windmill seem to have survived, and the two that illustrate this account were loaned by members of the Long Buckby Historical Society, for which Mr Philip Davis has my gratitude. However, Stanley Freese and G. N. Shann both commented on the existence of a photograph of the windmill taken before the

Frank C. Gill's sketch of Long Buckby post mill in 1901. [Reproduced with permission of R.C. Gill]

roundhouse was added. Such a photograph would be highly prized by the Society.

Another picture, this time a drawing, appeared in Frank Gill's 1928 article 'The Vanishing Windmill'. Gill portrayed the mill in working order (the drawing was made many years before) but depicted the sails much shorter than they should have been. Albert Amos, a local man and old friend of the author, described the sweeps as 'daisy cutters', almost touching the ground. 'Bert' also recalled that for a while the post mill was in the possession of Charles Townsend, whose grandson still lives in Long Buckby.

NASEBY POST MILL

It is well documented that during the decisive Civil War battle fought at Naseby in 1645, Charles I witnessed the defeat of his forces from the open trestle post mill that once stood three quarters of a mile north of the village in an area still known as 'Mill Hill'. A detailed, almost contemporary print, entitled 'A Representation of the Armies of King Charles I and Sir Thomas Fairfax', curiously depicts the windmill situated behind the Roundhead lines. At this point it is tempting to capitalize on sentiment by claiming (as has sometimes been believed) that this was the post mill demolished just after the First World War. Such an account would suggest apathy and ignorance on the part of the mill's then owners. However, such an account would not be true.

In 1792 the Reverend John Martin published a history of Naseby in which he stated that the 'Mill Hill' mill was destroyed by fire around 1732 along with a great quantity of wheat and flour. It had previously undergone extensive and costly repairs. Also

Naseby post mill in 1891 with sail cloths neatly furled. [Photo: Hove Public Library]

From an undated postcard showing the mill's long tailpole.
[Photo: Nigel Moon]

A sketch of Naseby mill in 1918 by Frank C. Gill, one year before it was felled. [Reproduced with permission of R.C. Gill]

mentioned was a second post mill which had been erected south of the village seven years earlier in 1725. The construction site was situated in the centre of a field on the eastern side of the road to Thornby, within a mile of Naseby. The location had once been a 'Chapel of Ease' (Knutcote Church, according to Herbert E. S. Simmons) and during the excavation work human bones were unearthed.

Many classic features were incorporated into the newly completed mill, including an open trestle that was supported on brick piers about a foot in height. The square buck was horizontally boarded and finished with a curved, rather than ogee, roof. Four clockwise common sails drove the mechanism and, conforming to the county's tradition, the body was manually turned into wind by means of a tailpole.

Naseby windmill was acknowledged by Thomas Jefferys, on whose map it was shown in 1779, but it was omitted from the Greenwood map of 1825/26 and the Ordnance Survey map of 1834.

Unfortunately, trade directories before 1847 only give details concerning major towns and villages, and Naseby was not to be found amongst them. Kelly's edition of 1847 recorded Nehemiah Ilston as miller, who was eventually replaced in 1864 or 1865 by the Coles family, and Elijah Coles was listed in the Royal directory of 1866. Before long George Coles was running the mill, with help from brothers, or possibly sons, Joseph in 1874 and Ilstowe in 1885. (Wright's directory of 1884 lists the miller as 'Illston Coles' which leaves one wondering if this may have been a misinterpretation of Ilstowe Coles.)

By 1890 Thomas Leeson was operating the windmill, but four years later he had been succeeded by Joseph Linnet, Naseby's last miller. Mr Linnet was documented as working with steam power in 1903, and much later in 1920, indicating an independent steam mill rather than an auxiliary power unit based at the post mill. The windmill itself seems to have ceased work around 1900, but it remained in a fair condition, as was verified by the artist and writer Frank C. Gill, who depicted it as it appeared in May 1918 intact with its four sails. His article was published in the *Northampton County Magazine* of 1928 under the title 'The Vanishing Windmill' chronicling the rise and fall of wind-powered mills, using those of Northamptonshire as an example.

One year after Gill made his drawing, in 1919, Naseby windmill was demolished. It was one of many post mills that fell victim to the destructive purges that were commonplace before 1920. After the mill's demolition many local craftsmen salvaged numerous timbers to manufacture reproduction antique furniture, a sickening irony for a genuine antique to be sacrificed to produce fakes.

The fine photograph of the mill accompanying this account, showing it in all its glory, was taken by Mr John Gregory in September 1891, and was eventually passed on to the Hove Public Library, Sussex, where I was lucky enough to obtain a copy.

The story does not finish here, for although the mill site south of the village now serves as farmland, the historic northern location at 'Mill Hill' and the battlefield are threatened by excavations for the A1/M1 link road. For Naseby the battle goes on.

NEWNHAM TOWER MILL

Standing 640 feet above sea level upon the summit of Newnham Hill is the extremely isolated tower of the village's windmill, situated on the western side of a meadow amongst undulating countryside. To the west of it the land falls steeply away into a furze sprinkled valley, and presents to the eye a breathtaking landscape. In complete contrast is the view from the road of the massed radio masts about Daventry, reminding us that for the moment progress has passed by this small area.

In its commanding situation Newnham mill resembles the locations of two other windmills — Hellidon (see page 68 and Napton-on-the-Hill in Warwickshire — both of which have been converted into dwellings. Newnham, also converted, differs in that it has recently been reconstructed as an observation tower. Anyone caring to borrow the keys to the building, which are held in Daventry, can expect to be treated to an all-round view made possible by a set of steps leading to the top floor which comprises a glazed area built on top of the original tower, the whole structure crowned with a nine-sided (enneahedral) roof. New doors and the general improvement to the mill show that the new owner takes a pride in the old building, and he has re-created the mill to look as it did at the beginning of the century. At that time the windmill had been out of use for many years and, although much of the gear was missing, it is claimed that the poll end could be seen beneath the roof — said by local man Russell Key to have been ten-sided (decahedral).

Much has changed since it was first seen by the author in 1980. At that time the stump was estimated to be approximately 22 or 23 feet in height, with the red brick left untarred and without any evidence of cement rendering. Much of the top was in a ruinous condition, and many fallen bricks littered the site. An internal inspection revealed the base diameter measured 15 feet 10 inches, with a wall thickness of 18 $1/2$ inches, although after ascending 1 foot 8 inches the thickness decreased to 14 inches to produce an internal ledge. The tower was also calculated to have a constant batter of 6.9 degrees, and generally one could not help being reminded of another Northamptonshire tower mill in a similar state at Barby (see page 24).

Like Barby, Newnham mill has a fireplace set in the ground-floor wall (in the latter's case with a flue rising to an opening near the eastern first floor window) and a brick floor, much of it broken up over the years through its use as a cattle shed. The author recalls that his first attempts, with a friend, to obtain measurements at this mill had to be abandoned. At the time the meadow around the tower was thick with heifers, and after battling through them we were shocked to find no less than four of the creatures within the building. No amount of persuasion would move them, and we were forced to leave. A later visit, without cattle present, compensated for the previous disappointment. There was no machinery or flooring, with the exception of a narrow beam bricked into the original mortises of a long lost first floor beam. This proved to be nothing more than a plank set on edge with a rope at its centre acting as a children's swing. However, to the west of the mill, down the slope, a decaying beam

Newnham mill with decahedral roof before World War I. [Photo: From an old postcard]

was discovered amongst some bracken. A row of neatly spaced mortises identified it as one of the principal floor beams.

Newnham mill was absent from the 1779 county map, but it could be found on Bryant's map of 1824-26 within a heavily shaded area of Newnham Hill. 'Newnham Windmill' is also marked on the 1834 Ordnance Survey map. The tower itself was constructed during the early nineteenth century by the Haynes family to replace another windmill (possibly a post mill) which had been located a quarter of a mile south-west of its successor.

The ruined stump in 1980 with 'those cows'! [Photo: The author]

This replacement stood three storeys high with four sails, and the stones were situated on the first floor, but unfortunately it is not certain what type of cap and method of winding was used. What is known, though, is that the windmill and watermill, which stood south of the village, were owned by the Haynes family who are believed to have leased them out during the late eighteenth and early nineteenth centuries, one of their tenants being Mr Thomas Garner, whose name appears in the 1840 and 1841 directories. Not long afterwards the family had taken over operations at Newnham themselves.

By 1847 William Haynes was recorded as the miller, and in 1854 James Haynes, who had previously held the windmill at Burrow Hill near Daventry, had taken charge. Between 1854 and 1864 James died leaving (presumably) his widow, Ann, to carry on the business as was customary in those days. With help from her son, Ann Haynes undertook the running of not only the windmill but also the watermill. This is verified in the directory for 1885 which recorded Ann Haynes as working the watermill only. One can only guess that this was around the time when the tower mill ceased work. Ann was again chronicled as a watermiller until some time just after 1894. Four years later Miss F. Haynes had taken charge of the watermill, and was still producing as late as 1906.

During the later part of the nineteenth century or early twentieth century an attempt was made to preserve the derelict structure, perhaps as a store. An early photograph shows the sail-less tower at its full height with a ten-sided roof which is believed by the author to have been a replacement for the original cap.

After repair work in 1988. [Photo: The author]

Looking much as it did at the beginning of the century, Newnham tower mill has been restored as a conversion. [Photo: The author]

Memories of the old mill could be found in the spring edition of the 1984 parish magazine in which the late Mr Russell Key recalled his first visit to the site 70 years previously, before the rotting ladders became unsafe and when one could still reach the second floor. He remembered that by this time the roof had collapsed, but one could still see the windshaft amid the debris. Mr Key wrote: 'More interesting to us was the discovery of candles, crockery, food and other evidence that at least the first floor was useful for tramps and, as we discovered later, for clandestine meetings.' Despite the sinister implications it is now known that the ruin was a favourite meeting place for lovers who, no doubt, took full advantage of the privacy offered by the isolated building. Russell also remembered that a village elder had told him that sometimes flour would be delivered from the windmill all the way to Daventry by workers carrying the sacks on their backs!

In May 1934 Karl S. Wood immortalized the mill in a drawing showing it in much the same condition as described above by Russell Key. Three years later G. N. Shann referred to the building as 'the ruined base of a tower mill ...' A study of the remains carried out by 'Syd' Simmons in April 1944 revealed that by this time the structure had been gutted, and the only piece of equipment to be found within was a single 4 foot 4 inch diameter peak stone at the doorway. Mr Simmons also noted that the positions of the three floors could still be traced.

In the recent past the land upon which the mill stands was believed to have been owned by the Anglian Water Authority. The tower itself had suffered greatly during its abandonment, and by 1980 the second floor had crumbled almost to the top level of the windows. Thankfully, the new owner carried out extensive repairs to the brickwork and the interior. The two ground floor window-ways were bricked up, and the doorways temporarily sealed with corrugated iron. By 1989 work had begun on the new roof, and now the heightened structure can be easily seen from the A361.

Apart from the filled-in first floor windows, a small hole, also bricked up near the chimney, can be seen and it is possible that this was once an aperture for a shaft driven by an external auxiliary engine. Unfortunately no corroborating evidence of this can be found.

NORTHAMPTON TOWER MILL

The last surviving Northampton windmill stands within the Kingsthorpe district which was originally a separate parish until its amalgamation with Northampton in 1900. The mill, a three storey stone-built tower mill is situated in Windmill Terrace just off the Boughton Green road. It is believed to stand 42 feet high and have a ground floor wall 3 feet thick, tapering to 1 foot 9 inches at its top.

'The Old Windmill', as it is known by its owners, has now been converted into a dwelling with two large extensions at its north-western and south-eastern points. Other additions include a spacious conservatory and a chimney stack rising from its

Kingsthorpe tower mill, Northampton, before 1904, standing upon its walled mound. [Photo: Mr & Mrs R.W. Campbell]

*Despite the loss of its
fantail, the mill still seems
to be in working order, as is
indicated by the furled
sailcloths.
[Photo: R.T. Walker]*

ground floor to the flat roof. The ground floor, now the lounge, has an internal diameter of 20 feet and betrays some signs of its windmill past. Two large oak beams span the lounge ceiling, one of them bearing the initials 'J.C.' and a geometric symbol. Some writing is also evident, but it is faint and could not be deciphered. A fireplace, dating from the time of the mill's conversion, remains but is no longer used as the owners have installed a more efficient heating system.

From this level, winding stairs lead to a first floor bedroom, then on to the attic where the diameter at this level is 14 feet 6 inches. With the aid of a ladder one can reach a trap door in the roof. From the top one can still obtain a fine view, even

The converted Northampton tower mill in the 1940s. [Photo: Donald Muggeridge]

though many newly built houses are situated near Windmill Terrace.

Generally the owners have succeeded in reflecting the character of the mill internally, and visitors are greeted with sights of varnished wood, horse brasses and tasteful furniture. It is somewhat reminiscent of a rural cottage, or the lounge of a

In 1989 with added extensions. [Photo: The author]

98

One of five surviving peak stones found in the gardens. [Photo: The author]

country pub, and in complete contrast to the pink and mauve paint schemes and false ceilings that confronted the couple when they first purchased the conversion.

In conversation with the occupants the author learned that living in a windmill was not without its problems. The flat roof allows rain to collect around the trap door, eventually causing dampness on the second floor level. One solution proposed by the owners was to install a copy of the original dome cap on top of the tower. There were hopes that fake sails might be included in the plans, but the scheme proved too expensive. However, it is hoped that at some future date construction of a cap will take place.

Five millstones (Derbyshire peaks) can be found in the garden, three of them incorporated within a low wall. Another piece of Kingsthorpe mill's past is in the shape of a small wooden wheel or pulley said to have once been attached to one of the ground floor beams. The wheel is kept away from the main house as unfortunately it has now been overwhelmed by woodworm.

The tower mill probably replaced an earlier windmill that appeared on the Eyre and Jefferys map of 1779, standing east of the present site. The later mill was recorded on Bryant's 1824-26 map. This was subsequently repeated on other maps including the 1835 Ordnance Survey. At that time the mill boasted four sails, a dome cap, fitted with a petticoat and a fan cradle carrying an eight-bladed fan. The clockwise sweeps comprised two common and two spring sails, the mechanism of which was contained in boxes fixed to the whip (see Barnack post mill on page 145).

The whole structure seems to have stood upon a mound lined by a stone wall, similar to that of Easton-on-the-Hill tower mill (see page 58). Kingsthorpe mill may have worked in co-operation with one of the watermills that operated within the parish. Unfortunately, the earlier trade directories did not distinguish between water, wind or steam mills. Those millers listed at Kingsthorpe (but not necessarily at the windmill) included C. Fitzhugh in the 1847 directory, J. C. Barrett in the 1869 edition, Thomas Moss in 1877, Matthew Warren in 1885, previously listed at Boughton watermill, and Thomas Spencer in the 1890 and 1894 volumes.

In 1904 the windmill was purchased by Mr Thomas Wilson, an ex-shoemaker who had recently returned from America with his bride, Elizabeth Connolly from Massachusetts. He set up a small building firm, and within a short time had altered the mill into a house. Spacious extensions were constructed but the tower remained the central part of the house. To the tower itself Thomas added the chimney stack, enlarged the window ways and lined the top of the tower wall with uneven stones giving it a 'ragged' appearance. It was Thomas Wilson's first building project and was the beginning of a successful career. In later years the windmill was to be adopted as a company symbol, and this was used throughout the 1920s and 30s.

In 1905 Thomas Wilson constructed his first house, for his brother-in-law. It was named 'Hillcrest' and was situated not far from the house conversion. That same year Elizabeth gave birth to a son at the mill. Connolly Thomas was named after his parents and eventually followed his father into the business. C. T. ('Con') Wilson played a leading role in expanding the firm into the large company of Wilson (Connolly) Holdings plc that still carries out much of the county's major building work. During this time 'Con' Wilson was a boxing promoter, and later became Chairman of Northampton Town Football Club. In 1955 he was awarded the O.B.E., and in 1970 after a rewarding life Connolly Wilson died.

At some time in the early post war years the Wilson home was sold to Mr George Gibson who, during the next ten years, was to carry out many modifications to the conversion. Mr Gibson claimed a total of £1,000 (a vast sum at that time) was spent on improvements including a new bathroom, garages, doors and windows. Further alterations were undertaken by the current owners who are justly proud of their historic Grade 2 listed home.

NORTHAMPTON WINDPUMP

Within Northampton just off the A428 Bedford Road stands the busy Out Patients Department of Northampton General Hospital, a relatively recent addition (constructed in the early 1970s) to the main hospital. Prior to this the site had been a noted beauty spot known as Vigo Gardens. The grounds were graced by a mansion, exotic gardens and a converted three-storeyed stump of an eighteenth century windmill, which should actually be referred to as a windpump. The historical importance of the conversion as Northampton's first practical water pumping station was frequently overlooked.

A main riverside area with the 'Nun Mills' south of the Nene and the now preserved 'Becket's Well' situated not far from a watermill built between 1560 and 1580 was known as 'Clack Mill'. It was here in 1702 that a spring of Chalybeate water was discovered near the Bedford Road in Cow Meadow. There were many claims that the water was of exceptional quality, and local people believed it was responsible for curing ailments. Indeed, the idea was put forward to make Northampton an official spa. The finding coincided with the wartime victory of the British and Dutch navies

A sketch based on L.A. Clarke's photograph of the converted tower which appeared in the Northampton Independent *in November 1937.*

One of R.M. Warwick's collection taken in early 1970. The bus is a Leyland Leopard of 1962 vintage, while in the background Vigo House can be seen with the ivy covered stump to the rear of the bus.
[Photo: R.M. Warwick]

over the French and Spanish fleets at the Port of Vigo in Spain. In celebration of the event the spring was thereafter known as the Vigo. It was many years later that the name was officially adopted.

Captivated with the notion of exploiting the recent find, Mr William Wykes of Hazelbeech, who was at that time Member of Parliament for Northampton, had constructed at great personal expense the town's first municipal water works. The idea was that the water would be pumped via a system of pipes to the market square and be collected, no doubt in troughs. A 'wind engine' was built in 1719 to provide the power.

At the ceremony organized to celebrate the completion of the scheme the Mayor of Northampton drank and declared the water to be good. His pronouncement was met with a peal of church bells and much cheering.

There are few drawings of the windpump, but a detail from Noble and Butlin's map of the town, drawn up in 1746, depicts the mill as having four sails and an ogee cap. It is known it stood three storeys high and was constructed of locally quarried stone blocks, described as 'ruddy Northampton sandstone'. The internal base diameter is reputed to have been 30 feet and the wall thickness at this level 18 inches. It seems common sails would have been in use at this time. This is verified by the writer G. J. De Wilde who in 1768 noted in his *Rambles Roundabout* that a 'windmill close to Vigo was in full sail', which probably refers to cloth-covered sweeps.

How the sails were brought into wind, and the method of pumping, are not known for certain, but winding may have been carried out by a Dutch-type tailpole fitting, or the winch and chain system of rotating the cap. (The automatic fantail was not invented until 1745.) As for the practice of pumping the water I must confess to pure guesswork. Taking into consideration that the scoop wheel method was already well established in the Fenland districts, one could be forgiven for believing the idea may have been incorporated within the windpump at Vigo. Another possibility could have involved the kind of lift pump common to the later skeleton-type wind machines.

There has been some speculation that the watermill was used in conjunction with supplying water to the town. Whether or not this is true, by 1745 the whole scheme had been abandoned.

The windpump was not allowed to fall into decay, and more than likely was altered and put to other use, as verified by De Wilde's 1768 description of the working windmill. That same year Clack Mill, which was then a paper mill, was badly damaged in a fire. Work continued, for in the Sun Fire Insurance policy of November 1780 the paper mill was mentioned along with the mill house, a drying shed and the windpump (actually referred to as a 'stone smock' windmill). The windmill was insured together with its going gears for £70. A reference to Clack Mill some three years later claimed that it was being used for paper-making and capable of working by either water or wind! In 1788 both mills were recorded as corn mills.

The name Vigo had by the 1820s been fully adopted for the area. Both mills were thereafter known as the 'Vigo mills' when spoken of together, with the watermill retaining its individuality and continuing to be called 'Clack Mill'. Apparently the name derived from the sound of a small gear at work. To quote Mr Beeby Thompson from *Northampton County Magazine* of 1931: '... a small toothed wheel attached to the upper millstone to jog the feeding trough or funnel, and so keep up a continuous feed of corn to the stones.' Within the mechanism of the average underdrift windmill, a spindle known as the damsel would have performed the same task. At a later date the watermill became renamed 'Mulliner's Mill'.

By 1830 the property was owned by Mr John Charles Barrett, although it was William Barrett who was listed within James Pigot and Co.'s National Commercial Directory of that year as a 'brickmaker' based at 'Vigo Mill'. Under 'millers' he was also recorded as operating at Nun Mill, just a few hundred yards south of the Vigo. In August 1830 the estate was put up for sale by John Barrett. The advertisement carried in *The Northampton Mercury* reported the sale of 'Vigo Tea Gardens' and catalogued the property including the house, working corn watermill with three pairs of stones, granaries, storage sheds, stables, a brickyard and a round tower or cottage. The account continued to give a lavish description of the attractive gardens which were regarded with much admiration. The spacious garden was adorned with flower beds, trees and shrubs, an ornamental lake and a bowling green all reached by gravel paths. In later years other additions were made, including a large rose garden (the filled-in mill pond), a tennis court, date palms and a sunken garden said to be the finest rockery in the country. The secret of the garden's success was the fertile soil enriched by the spring water. Even a near drought in the summer of 1921 failed to cause any major problems.

Surrounded by all this, one can understand that the ugliness of the nearby Vigo brickyard may have been a deciding factor in Mr Barrett's decision to sell. A stunning photograph of the brickyard taken in 1896 appears in the book *Life in Old*

1. Windpump/mill
2. Vigo House
3. East Lawn
4. Lower Garden
5. Tennis Court
6. Site of 'Clack Cottages'

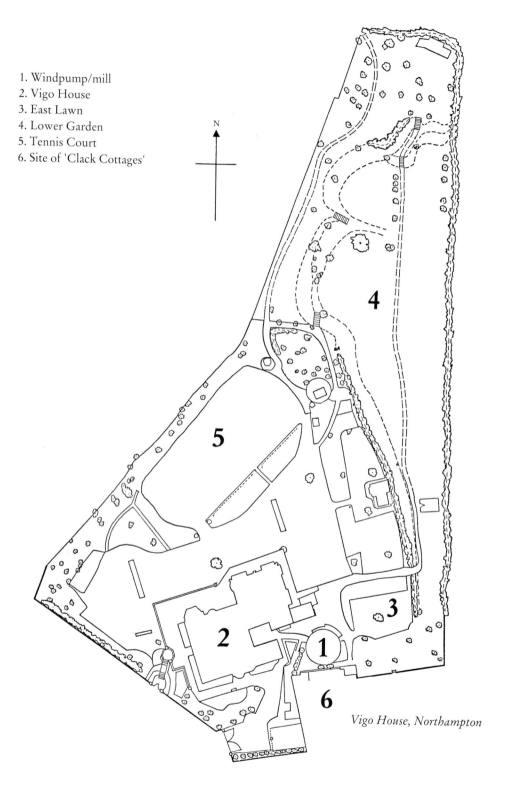

Vigo House, Northampton

Northampton published in 1976 by Northamptonshire Libraries. The picture reveals a huge quarry of some 30 feet deep very near the Bedford Road.

The 'Round Tower' or 'Cottage' mentioned in the sale notice of 1830 confirms that the windpump had by this time been converted into a dwelling. External modifications would have included the removal of the cap and sails, but it seems the tower was left at its original height and a flat roof added. Within, all the gear was ripped out and a spiral staircase was fitted. Fireplaces were installed on the first and second floors, according to reports (no mention is made of the ground floor), and a chimney built on to the tower's northern side. It is known that during the 1850s Mr John Henry Gulliver lived in the conversion for a total of seven years. At another time the building was inhabited by Mr Samuel Budd, a Chelsea Pensioner.

In 1837 the Northampton Water Works was established at nearby Cliftonville, and eventually was responsible for draining the supply of water to Clack Mill. Grinding continued until some time between the late 1830s and mid 1840s, but it was not long before the old watermill succumbed to progress and was eventually replaced by a group of terraced houses known as either the 'Vigo' or 'Clack' cottages.

The mill pond existed in 1846. A plan of the area shows that the water extended up to the converted windpump's eastern side, allowing a narrow path for access. Before being filled-in the mill pond was a popular attraction for local anglers.

Apart from the gardens, the most interesting feature of the area was Vigo House itself. The small country mansion stood close to the windpump and was only two storeys in height. There was only one flight of stairs, no cellar and no attic. One part of the house, built in the early eighteenth century, suffered from settlement. However, the tilting floors that resulted seemed not to upset the owners to any great extent.

There, from 1890, Mr and Mrs C. R. Nunn enjoyed 27 years of spacious living, but it was Mr and Mrs H. W. Hanwell who undertook major modifications to the house and grounds from the time they moved in during 1917. Illustrations of the ground floor rooms from the *Northampton Independent* of 1922 reveal large panelled rooms adorned with pictures, plaques etc. Within the billiard room a seventeenth century fireplace had been installed, salvaged from a London mansion. The overmantle was said to have been the largest Chippendale known to exist. The Hanwells were great collectors of ceramics, pride of place going to a number of Ming vases. Large bay windows gave a good view of the garden, and the now ivy-covered conversion.

Other alterations included the construction of the sunken garden, and the fitting of two large ground floor windows into the northern side of the converted windpump. There was much excitement when it was discovered the tower was being inhabited by nesting tawny owls. Further repairs to the tower were carried out during the late 1920s by the then owner Mr Egerton Speakman. It has been claimed that the Rice family, who ran the Northampton-based foundry, occupied Vigo House for a while, but by 1937 it was owned by architect Mr Arthur Henson.

In November of that same year the *Northampton Independent* published a picture of the conversion taken by Mr L. A. Clarke. The photograph showed the stump standing possibly three storeys in height with a balcony at what may have been the second floor. Foliage just forward of the conversion prevents an accurate assessment of its true height, even though the building was stripped of its ivy covering. The article was one of a series entitled 'Unsuspected Northampton', and even then gave the impression that local people were ignorant of its existence.

The last owner of Vigo gardens was Dr I. H. Gosset who bought the property in 1947. Astonishingly, he was informed that the original sails were stored in the lofts of the nearby terraced houses. Dr Gosset never had reason to investigate the claim, so sadly the truth will never be known as the area was redeveloped about 1963 to accommodate the extending United Counties bus garage. If the story of the sails is true one can only assume that for years they were perhaps stored within the watermill, and upon its destruction transferred to the newly built cottages. One of the terraced houses was used for storage by the Civil Defence during the Second World War.

In a letter to the author, Dr Gosset's son, Mr W. P. Gosset, recalled as a child being prevented from entering the tower as it was felt the structure was unsafe. Dr Gosset was particularly concerned about an external staircase which led to the balcony. The doctor's suspicions later proved well founded when in 1960 part of the internal floors collapsed. From that time onwards the building was used as a storage shed. Mr W. P. Gosset stated in his letter he could only remember the conversion having a ground and first floor, so if and when the tower was truncated is still uncertain.

Although photographs of the conversion have proved elusive, I have seen a number of pictures taken by Mr R. M. Warwick of Northampton, an author and enthusiast on the subject of buses. Mr Warwick was employed in the Records Department at United Counties and photographed many of the company's fleet, often using the stump as a backdrop. Two such photographs display single and double decker buses from the late 1950s to early 60s period, parked near a wall with the tower peeping over the top. Some 'Counties' personnel mistook the stump for the base of a large industrial chimney.

Before the whole site was levelled for redevelopment in early 1990 three terraced houses existed within the bounds of the bus garage. Knocked into one, they were used as administration offices. Remembering the fate of the sails the author asked his elder brother, at that time an employee at the garage, to investigate the possibility of further remains from the windpump's past lurking within their lofts. Unfortunately, nothing more was discovered.

The end came in 1970 when Dr Gosset sold the grounds to the Northamptonshire Health Authority. The house, gardens and the windpump were levelled, stones from the tower being broken up for hardcore. Only part of the garden wall and the entrance gates were spared. During the demolition a water course was discovered at the tower's southern point. A team of archaeologists was recruited to investigate, and they later reported that it was connected with the old windpump. No thought was given to preservation, and nowadays even the name 'Vigo' is rarely used.

OUNDLE TOWER MILL

A windmill at Oundle can be traced back as far as 1736 in the Court Rolls which include mention of the 'Windmill Field' in possession of Thomas Cross. Eventually this land was left to Thomas's son John who set about the construction of a new windmill near the Glapthorn Road, probably to replace the former mill. By 1739 the property, described as 'newly erected' had passed to William Pendred, but unfortunately he was soon declared bankrupt, and the windmill together with the surrounding land was purchased by John Hewson for 300. Some years later in 1806 Hewson put the mill up for sale, and in the advertisement the tower mill was described as a 'capital stone-built smock windmill with two pairs of stones, a six foot flour

Oundle tower mill during its working days. The sails and fan were removed in 1908. [Photo: Alice Thomas]

By 1935 the mill still retained its machinery, as is evident from the poll end still being in situ. [Photo: Donald Muggeridge]

machine, and a flour mill.'

As with many tower mills found throughout the county, Oundle mill stood only three storeys high, and complying with its surroundings it had been constructed of locally quarried limestone. Another name given to the material was 'Blisworth stone', even though the quarries themselves were in the parish of Oundle. A second notable feature was the set of clockwise turning sails, generally said to be less common than the anti-clockwise arrangement. However, a large number of windmills in the county adopted this system. The sweeps themselves were patents, obviously replacing an earlier set some time after 1807. These were brought into wind by an eight-bladed fantail mounted behind a conical cap.

The mill was again referred to, by its owner Robert Brown, as a 'capital stone-built smock mill' in a 'For Sale' advert in *The Stamford Mercury* of 23 June 1809. After some months delay it was a lady, Susannah Ragsdell, a baker, who afforded the price of £740. Unlike many of her predecessors, Mrs Ragsdell held the property for almost a decade until her death, and it then passed to her son Richard in 1820. By 1828 the premises had been acquired by the Callow family who also owned the wind and water mills at Castor near Peterborough (see page 159). The 1824 Ordnance Survey map shows that the mill enjoyed a secluded existence, but in 1836 it was proposed to construct a workhouse not far from the mill site. The project was contested by William and John Thomas Callow, younger brothers of Robert, the original owner. They claimed that the workhouse would interfere with the flow of air to the mill, but despite their protests the scheme went ahead. Whether or not the workhouse affected the mill's performance is not recorded, but by 1841 John T. Callow had decided to sell or let the property. A possible tenant may have been Hosea Bradford, chronicled as 'miller of Oundle' in the 1841 census. Another tenant (or employee) was William Bowman Francis who learned his skills at Oundle before taking a post at a Lincolnshire mill. Unfortunately it was not enough to prevent him from insolvency, and in 1844 he was sent to the debtors prison in Lincoln. W. Baker was listed as the 'miller of Oundle' in the 1847 directory, but within two years it had passed to landowner John Smith. This ambitious man eventually purchased the tower mill and the surrounding land from the Callows and resumed work. With help from his son, also called John, Mr Smith prepared for the busiest part of 1855, just after the September harvest. At some time during early October a strong gale hit Oundle and ripped off two of the mill's sweeps. Although a serious inconvenience the setback did little to diminish his enthusiasm for the business and the mill remained in the family's possession for the next two decades. In 1876 William North, described as 'master miller' in a later census, bought the windmill together with a number of other buildings for £200.

By 1885 John William North, his son, was running the mill, and it was he who left the property to Mrs Mary Jane Perkins (possibly his daughter) in 1894. The firm of North and Perkins continued operations at Glapthorne Road for many years even after the sails were damaged and eventually removed in 1908. The directories for 1920 and 1928 record that grinding was still taking place at Oundle with the aid of a gas engine. It was clear that by the mid-1930s work had ceased at the Glapthorn Road mill, though North and Perkins were listed as late as 1940 dealing in the sale of various animal feeds and as agents for Carter's seeds.

In 1932 the tower was seen by windmill artist Karl S. Wood, whose sketch of the mill displayed some damage to the cap. Little had changed when Herbert Simmons inspected the site four years later. At that time the building was owned by Mr E. D. Perkins, and within his notes 'Syd' Simmons was able to describe its brief history and some parts of its equipment. The fantail had gone, probably removed at the same time as the sails, but the three pairs of stones, one French and two peak, remained. Also in place was the wire machine, but unfortunately no mention was made of the principal machinery. It was noted in 1944 that the tower was empty of gear. One assumes that it had been scrapped and any metal requisitioned for war use.

Although it did not feature on the 1954 Ordnance Survey map, the windmill survived until 1964 when its owner, Mr Crawley, had it demolished. Thankfully the memory of the old mill lives on through the efforts of Mrs Alice Thomas and other local historians, and a fine photograph of the working mill can be found upon the back cover of *Old Oundle: a Pictorial History* published by the Rotary Club of Oundle.

Raunds tower mill during repairs and maintenance to the sails and fantail.
[Photo: Cyril Putt]

RAUNDS TOWER MILL

Located half a mile west of the town, Raunds tower mill was built on the site of a post mill which appeared upon the 1798 enclosure map of the parish. The schedule described the plot as a windmill and homestead in the occupation of Mary Throssell. A more detailed illustration, depicting an open trestle post mill with four sails, appeared on an impropriate tithe allotment map of the following year. It was also recorded on Jefferys' county map of 1779 and subsequent maps, including the 1825/26 Greenwood map and the 'First Edition' of the Ordnance Survey of 1835. One of the earliest millers whose name has come to light was Mr John Throssell, who died in 1790.

The date when the post mill was succeeded by the tower cannot be determined. An inscribed datestone existed but was sadly destroyed when the tower's remains were demolished in 1964, and unfortunately no record of the inscription was made. The last miller's grandson, Mr Roy Pentelow, who lives in Raunds, recalls that his father had always claimed to have been born on the date of the windmill's centenary in 1894. This would imply that the tower mill was erected in 1794, but this is inconsistent with the appearance of a post mill on the early maps. At this stage a credible solution cannot be found.

Standing just west of the church, together with a millhouse and stables, Raunds mill was a handsome structure built of stone, rising five floors to the curb and crowned with a white ogee cap with a ball finial atop a long stalk. Unusually for an ogee cap, it had a gallery. Such a fitting was regarded as a mixed blessing by millers, for although it provided ready access to the cap and fantail, it interfered with the flow of wind to the fan. This problem did not exist during the windmill's early life, for it is believed Raunds mill was manually turned into the wind by means of a tailpole extending to the ground from the cap, as was the case at Easton-on-the-Hill (see page 58). Eventually this system was replaced by the more efficient automatic fantail, and in this case a six-bladed version was installed. The sails consisted of four anti-clockwise patents claimed to have been fitted sometime after 1807. One noticeable break from convention was the use of the double-shuttered type rather than the more commonplace single-shuttered sail so often found in the county. Within the tower, which was only partly tarred, there were three stone pairs, two sets of French burrs and one pair of Derbyshire peaks. During the 1890s the wind power was augmented by steam, and a pulley was installed in one of the ground floor window ways, being driven from a portable steam engine.

For many decades Raunds tower mill was owned by the Pentelow family who moved to the town from Huntingdonshire in 1839 and immediately took up residence in the old millhouse. In 1841 James Pentelow, then aged 35, held the windmill, and by 1843 was seeking an apprentice miller. A suitable applicant was found in the shape of James Beeby of Raunds. In his work contract Mr Beeby was obliged to serve a period of three years commencing from October 1843. Amongst the terms agreed he was not

Mr James T. Pentelow and part of his family. [Photo: Roy Pentelow]

to 'do damage to his master', gamble, 'haunt taverns', marry or commit fornication! James Beeby completed his apprenticeship and later went on to operate the 'Little London' tower mill at Spalding.

In 1847 Mr J. Boyfield appeared in the county trade directory as the town's miller, but Mrs Elizabeth Pentelow and two of her sons, Job, aged 15, and John, aged 12, were the only millers to be found there in the 1851 census. That census did not include Mrs Pentelow's husband, merely noting the facts that she was married and described herself as a 'windmiller'. It appears to be reasonable to conclude that by that time she had been widowed, a conjecture which is reinforced by her appearance as the miller in the 1854 trade directory. It might have been that Mr Boyfield was employed by her for a time to help her operate the mill until her children became old enough to do so. The lady must have been an extremely busy woman, for as well as running the tower windmill she was mother to eight: five boys and three girls. Her two eldest sons, Job and John, subsequently took over the mill, and by 1864 Job Pentelow was recorded in the directory as working at the mill. He employed one man, possibly his 29-year-old younger brother Frederick, who described himself as a 'journeyman miller'. Job, then aged 34, lived in the mill house with his wife and their five children. The eldest son, James Thomas Pentelow, then 6 years old, was to go on to follow in his father's footsteps when the mill passed to him between 1890 and 1894.

Back in 1874 John Pentelow had been documented as the Raunds miller. However, it was his wife Maria who was so described in 1890. Job's son, James Thomas Pentelow, took over the business soon afterwards. By this time the wind had been supplemented by steam power. James and his wife, Sarah Jane, had an exceptionally large family of no less than twelve children! But the busy family life and established business were soon disrupted when tragedy struck. In October 1905 James Pentelow died after falling from the mill's gallery. He was 40 years of age. After the initial shock Mrs Pentelow carried on the work until she was forced to sell in 1906.

Raunds tower mill proudly displaying its anti-clockwise turning, double-shuttered, patent sails, and its six-bladed fantail. [Photo: Cyril Putt]

By 1934 the tower was no more than a truncation, empty of its machinery. Further alterations were made before its destruction in 1964. [Photo: Donald Muggeridge]

During October 1907 *The Miller* reported that Raunds mill had been withdrawn from auction to be privately sold to a Stanwick man, Mr Holland, for £400. He held the property for just over a year, then on 26 October 1908 a notice appeared in *The Miller* offering for sale the 'first class mill' which was described as a 'modern and solid erection'. Interested parties were invited to contact Mr W. F. Corby of Raunds.

It is believed that the windmill never worked again after leaving the Pentelow family. One of Raunds' most long-standing inhabitants, Mrs Alice Cox, recalled that the cap and other parts of the top of the structure were removed during the 1920s (the sails had been taken down in 1912.) Doubtless it was at this time that the mechanism went, and afterwards the tower was used as a store. It was in this condition that Karl S. Wood pictured it as a featureless tower. Two years later Stanley Freese and Donald Muggeridge recorded the mill as a three-floored derelict.

At some time, thought locally to have been after the Second World War, the remains were reduced in height to about 20 feet. Later a local farmer, who had just taken over a small firm of builders, purchased the remains and the surrounding land with the intention of developing it. Before the scheme was implemented, the company was dissolved, and the property passed to their creditors, a London finance company. In 1964 the last surface remains were cleared away and a small housing estate built upon the surrounding land. The foundations of the mill are said still to lie below the surface of the soil, a mere six inches deep, and on days when the weather is favourable a corresponding circle can be made out in the overlying grass.

Rushden smock mill sometime before the Great War. A number of interesting features can be seen in this photograph, including the boxes containing the springs for the spring sails (centre of the whip) and the adjusting levers at the sweep's tip. The wooden tower is covered in tarred felt, and the mobile steam engine is for windless days. [Photo: William Dilley]

RUSHDEN SMOCK MILL

A few yards from the Bedfordshire border, on the eastern side of the Wymington road stands the converted ground floor base of the county's last remaining smock mill. The eight-sided single storey building is painted white and has a tiled octahedral roof complete with a chimney stack. Large extensions have been added which disguise the base somewhat, but the name 'Mill Estate' confirms its former use.

The Wymington Road windmill, which is frequently but incorrectly referred to as 'Wymington' windmill, appears on Bryant's 1824 map standing beside a bridle-way. It was a superficially conventional smock mill with an octagonal horizontally boarded wooden tower, dome cap (with finial) and four sails. Other features included an eight-bladed fantail and a luffing wheel. Unusual was the protection applied to the weatherboarding of the two storey smock tower which consisted of a covering of tarred felt. This differed from the system employed at Northamptonshire's only other smock mill at Eye Green (see page 160) where the tower was clad in triple weatherboarding. Rushden mill's sails, too, deserve special mention, for not only did they revolve in a clockwise direction, but comprised two common sweeps and two spring. As in the cases of Barnack post mill (see page 144) and Kingsthorpe tower mill in Northampton (see page 96) the shutters were operated by levers at the sail's tip, and the springs were contained in boxes fitted to the centre of the whips.

George Judkins Aychurch was described as a miller and baker in Rushden around 1838. He almost certainly worked the Wymington Road smock mill because one Mr A. Aychurch did so in the mid-1840s. At this time the mill was copyhold to the noted Sartoris family of Rushden Hall, who probably employed subsequent millers including Mr T. Moore between 1854 and in the early 1870s, Stephen Hall and possibly George Walker.

In the years preceeding World War I the smock mill belonged to Mr and Mrs Lewis. The miller in 1903 was William Chapman who, within three years, was replaced by William Laurance. The latter undertook much of his own millwrighting, including dressing the stones. But Mr Laurance was not without help. Two young assistants, Frederick Dilley and his younger brother William helped Mr Laurance with the odd-jobs about the windmill, including setting the cloth and shuttered sails, and delivering the flour. When interviewed in 1980 at the advanced age of 81 William recalled that it was not unusual for Mr Laurance to lodge with the Dilley family, but this did not stop a young William from being chastised by the miller after being caught swinging from the fan cradle during a spell of boisterous horseplay. Mr Dilley remembered that during the mill's time it processed a variety of foodstuffs, including flour, kibling beans and bran. Towards the end of its life this principally would have been for livestock when wartime legislation forbade the selling of stone-ground flour for human consumption (see page 182). Meanwhile, the Great War had taken its toll. Soon after joining up, Frederick was killed during the bitter fighting in France, and William spent his sixteenth birthday in the trenches. William Laurance, however,

The base converted in 1934. [Photo: Donald W. Muggeridge]

As it is today, with added extensions. [Photo: The author]

found romance during those dark years, married and later left the district. After that, in about 1915, the windmill stopped working forever.

The windmill remained standing but disused until around 1920 when the sails and machinery were removed and the wooden tower dismantled. The base was converted and put up for sale by Mrs Lewis for £300. It was bought by William and Frederick's elder brother, John H. Dilley, and at a cost of £400 a roof was added by Messrs Farrows of Rushden. William Dilley had also married, and was living close by at the mill house which was known locally as the 'Red House' and stood adjacent to the base.

All of John Dilley's three children were born in the windmill's base. His youngest daughter is related to the current owner who acquired the property in 1963. Soon afterwards the building was renovated, and extensions were added after it was found that the base only measured 22 feet across, and proved to be very cramped. Although proud of his home, the owner told me that members of the public can prove to be something of a nuisance once discovering the house was part of a windmill. Hopefully readers will bear this in mind.

SCALDWELL POST MILL

Scaldwell has changed little since the time of the windmill. It is still noted as one of the few villages in the county without a public house but, as with many other small communities, there is a close-knit spirit tinged with pride in their surroundings. Few could tell much about the windmill, but all those to whom I spoke expressed a hint of regret that the old wooden structure was no longer standing. This is not hard to understand when one realizes that a windmill had existed at Scaldwell as far back as the thirteenth century, during the time of Henry III. That particular site was situated north-west of the village. Its eighteenth century descendant stood between half and three-quarters of a mile west of Scaldwell, and is known to have existed in 1775 when

An early photograph from the Kershaw collection of prints of the Scaldwell area, kept at the County Record Office, Delapre Abbey Northampton. Note the exernal pulley for additional power via a steam engine. [Photo: Northamptonshire Record Office]

Scaldwell mill shortly before it was pulled down in 1916. The sails show signs of damage, and the roundhouse roof has collapsed. [From an old postcard]

the owner, William Kirkham, was obliged to pay a forfeit of ten shillings a year to the local rector, church wardens and overseers; a practice which still continues to this day.

The mill appeared upon many early maps, including the Eyre and Jefferys map of 1779, Bryant's 1824-26 chart, and the 1835 Ordnance Survey. It was curiously absent from Greenwood's 1825/26 edition, but in all the other cases it was titled 'Scaldwell mill', and its location clearly depicted (on two of the three maps) with the post mill symbol.

During its working years the post mill was powered by four clockwise common sails, occasionally having to be brought into wind by means of a tailpole. The buck and curved roof were horizontally boarded, and the supporting trestle was enclosed within a single storey brick roundhouse. The whole structure rested upon a mound, 80 yards from the roadside. Not far from the mill was the miller's cottage, probably occupied by Richard Taylor, known to have been the miller during the 1850s. The mill subsequently passed to Mr J. Taylor, about 1863, but within a few years the Taylors were replaced by Mr G. Aychurch. George Clement soon followed in the 1870s, and Scaldwell's last miller was Thomas Dawson, who acquired the mill sometime between 1880 and 1890.

By 1906 the post mill had shut down and was derelict, although said to be in fairly good working order. This observation was made by Major C. A. Markham, and later featured in the journal *Northamptonshire Notes and Queries* of which he was the editor. In the January 1926 volume Markham claimed that the mill's breast was clad in sheets of iron plate, but it is possible tarred felt was used, as was the practice with other post mills.

The Major's article also contained a drawing of the building dated 26 July 1906. Unfortunately the picture was not without fault, the mill's buck being completely out of proportion with the roundhouse. It did display some interesting details, however.

The roundhouse featured two adjacent doorways, and some damage to the sails was evident.

Another version of the derelict mill was captured in a charming watercolour by J. A. Perrin which depicted the windmill upon its mound surrounded by grazing cattle and young girls picking flowers. Once again some inaccuracies are apparent, but in Perrin's case they seem to have been deliberate. The mill is shown with its sail stocks bare of sailframes, a long curving tailpole and a skirt just beneath the buck. A photograph from the same period paints a less glamorous picture of the windmill with battered sails, a short, straight tailpole and no skirt. The photograph reveals the partly collapsed roundhouse wall and the tarred, felted roof fallen around the trestle.

In the spring of 1916 Albert Watson, the owner, had the ruin demolished. The remains were sold to a local wheelwright, 'Jack' Corby, who re-used the timbers to make items of furniture. Scaldwell man Mr Brian Hensman (who supplied much information) still owns a wheelbarrow constructed from parts of the windmill during the late 1920s. Brian explained that the current owners of the site were retired farmers who had recently removed all traces of the mound, but were tied to tradition by retaining the yearly payment of ten shillings (fifty pence).

SILVERSTONE TOWER MILL

The windmill stands a quarter of a mile east of Silverstone, behind a farmhouse on the Whittlebury road. Now virtually an empty shell, it gives few clues to its varied past, but fortunately, thanks to the owner and other villagers, an unusual tale was pieced together. It was said that this mill was built to supplement or succeed a windmill that existed at Whittlebury. The new mill was constructed of red brick, three storeys high and carried four single-shuttered, anti-clockwise patent sails, a dome cap and a fantail. Unfortunately, the year of its erection is unclear as the tower itself bears no clues. It is absent from both the Bryant and Greenwood maps but does appear on the Ordnance Survey of 1833. The miller in 1847 was Mr G. Higham, but within a few years Mr W. Earle had seemingly taken over. By the late 1860s the mill was once again being worked by the Higham family, although this time it was Charles Higham who was charged with its running.

Silverstone tower mill during its working days. [Photo: B. Smith]

121

Silverstone mill as it appeared in the 1920s. [Photo: Maurice and Joyce Palmer]

At some time during the tower mill's life an incident occurred which has become almost folklore. A visitor to the farm was believed to have left his pony and trap in the mill field where the tower mill was working. After a while the grazing animal wandered closer and closer to the mill, until part of the harness was caught by the revolving sails. The horse, complete with trap, was snatched from the ground and taken up some feet in the air before the offending strap broke free, sending the unfortunate creature plummeting down. One hopes that the pony was merely shaken, but the fate of the animal is unknown.

Grinding at Silverstone came to a halt around the turn of the century. Although disused it remained complete until 1904 when miller Thomas Winkles purchased the four sails for his tower mill at Wootton (see page 139). After transporting and assembling the sweeps it was found to be necessary to reinforce them with a bowsprit and cables. In the meantime, Silverstone mill was left to the mercy of the elements. Some time later it was gutted with the exception of the upper machinery, including the windshaft. The cap deteriorated to such an extent that by the 1930s only some framing remained, and it was in this condition that Stanley Freese photographed it in July 1934, and Karl Wood sketched it in April 1939.

Just over a year later the whole country was gripped by war fever, and the fear of German seaborne and airborne landings. Newly formed Home Guard units commandeered weapons, vehicles and buildings in an effort to be ready to repel the potential invaders. Naturally, tall buildings were highly valued as observation posts, and Silverstone mill was earmarked to be used as such. To fit in with defenders' plans the windshaft had to be removed; then the headframe, complete with fan cradle, was rigged up to a tractor and dragged from the tower. Inside, a rickety wooden ladder fixed to the eastern wall led to the dust floor where a makeshift shelter had been constructed for the men on watch. The platoon, under command of a lieutenant who lived locally, formed part of the 13th Battalion (Towcester District) Home Guard who took responsibility for the security of Silverstone aerodrome (now the internationally famous motor racing circuit).

During the early 1980s when I first saw this mill I was pleased to note that the ladder and platform remained, although the shelter had been taken down some years before. Outside, a derelict Fordson tractor contributed to the scene of abandonment. A second visit nine years later met with failure as the owner refused to allow me in to take measurements (even though the customary letter explaining my intentions had been sent some weeks before). The owner claimed that he had suffered constant pestering by people wishing to view the mill at close quarters, and preferred it if he and the tower could be left in peace.

Although disappointed at the time, one cannot condemn such feelings as, after all, whether a house conversion or a shell, a windmill belongs to somebody, and enthusiasts should remember to respect the owner's wishes as well as their property.

Silverstone mill during the mid-1970s. Little had changed by 1989. [Photo: A.C. Smith]

123

SULGRAVE TOWER MILL

Now converted into a fine residence with spacious extensions, Sulgrave tower mill was not more than an empty shell when it was first seen by the author in April 1980. The mistake was made of approaching the mill from the village rather than the quicker and less muddy bridle-path from Culworth. After making my way past the watermill with its spring fed mill pond I eventually encountered the bridle-way which leads directly past the tower mill located in an area once known as 'Windmill Ground'.

Set within a circular hedged enclosure the shell stood three storeys high built of grey limestone, ornamented at door and window ways with red brick lintels. It is worth noting that the whole of the internal wall was of red brick, but Sulgrave mill's most stunning feature was, and still is, its slight batter, giving the tower an almost cylindrical appearance. Despite the customary fears that such an erection would be prone to cracking, or other forms of weakness, the structure seemed to be in good order, with the exception of the south-western ground floor window way which had succumbed to vandalism. Fortunately, the fallen stones remained at the base of the tower and had not been looted.

Visible from the B4525, the mill stands half a mile north-west of the village, which is forever linked with Sulgrave Manor and the venerable Washington family, the tombs of some members of which are to be found within the parish church. Most famous of all is George Washington, America's first president, but some of his descendants are associated with the mill. In 1539 Lawrence Washington was granted the parishes of Sulgrave and Woodford, which included the Manor; while some years later in 1600 Richard Washington rented a windmill from Lord Spencer.

John Prescott is known to have been the miller of 1629, but it is possible that the above may relate to an earlier windmill, and not the present structure, for although its appearance is primitive compared to other tower mills, the building is more likely (in the author's opinion) to be an eighteenth century creation. An enclosure award of 1761 mentions a mill then owned by Edward Brockless, and a windmill is illustrated at the present location on Eyre and Jeffreys' map of 1779. Although the windmill is evident on the Greenwood map of 1825/26 it was not mentioned in a sale notice in 1824. Only the watermill, dwelling house and bakery were documented

One interesting detail of the site's past can be found in the book *Sulgrave Manor and the Washingtons* published in 1933. In it the author, H. Clifford Smith, claimed the west doorway of the parish church originated from a Saxon church once located near the site of the present windmill. Mr Clifford Smith also mentions the nearby watermill, the pond of which was fed by springs known as 'Holy Well' and 'Vigo'. Both the watermill and the windmill were being run by the Course family in Victorian times. In 1854 Mr R. Course was recorded as the miller, and by 1861 the business had passed to Alfred Course, possibly the previous miller's son. The Post Office directory of 1869 identified Alfred as a miller and farmer, while Kelly's edition of 1877 listed him as a baker, in addition to his other two occupations.

The derelict shell of Sulgrave mill in 1980. [Photo: The author]

Rebuilding work, 1981. [Photo: The author]

Fully converted. [Photo: The author]

An advertisement in *The Miller* of 6 April 1885 proclaimed that both the wind and watermills were to be let. Both were said to have been in 'full trade', the watermill having an overshot wheel of 19 feet in diameter, whereas the tower mill was equipped with three pairs of stones. The mill house, bakery and other buildings, including stables, were also offered in the deal, along with 48 acres of land — although the directory for that year states that Mr Course worked with water and steam power only. This was repeated in the 1890 volume, and by 1894 Alfred was recorded as a farmer only. No further references to the mills were made after 1890, indicating they may have by that time ceased to work.

In 1980 few villagers remembered the tower mill in a derelict condition, but Colworth man, Mr Smith, could recall climbing the sails within the early years of this century. H. Clifford Smith had given a contemporary description of Sulgrave mill in his book of 1933 as 'sail-less and dilapidated'. This view was corroborated in July 1934 when Karl S. Wood pictured the remains with what he described as a 'pointed roof' in a ruinous condition. Author Stanley Freese photographed the derelict mill in May 1936, and a year later G. N. Shann gave a short but detailed account of the mechanism, claiming the mill had originally worked with spring sails of which no trace remained, indicating his source of information was either local intelligence or an old photograph. The machinery comprised a mixture of wooden and iron gear which had at one time powered the two pairs of under-driven stones. Shann made it clear that the mill had been winded with the aid of a 'Y' wheel and winch operated by an endless chain. This was contradicted by Herbert E. S. Simmons in July 1944, who claimed the remnants of a farm cradle were visible. Simmons went on to give a fine record of the internal mechanism as well as other details such as the lack of floorboards (although all of the principal beams remained).

On top of the tower's wall was a wooden curb with a rack of upward facing teeth. The windshaft was described as iron, as was the upright shaft, the difference being the former is said to have been round with a metal poll end, while the latter was 5 inches square. A timber built clasp-arm brake wheel with its iron teeth cast in sections would normally have engaged a wallower, but the all wood gearing had broken away from its position at the top of the upright shaft and could be seen laying across the dust floor beams. Just beneath this level attached to the shaft was a six-armed iron crown wheel with wooden teeth, 2 feet 6 inches in diameter. This might have driven the sack hoist or a dressing machine, but it will never be known for sure as Mr Simmons failed to expand upon its possible function.

Other details were well recorded, including the ground floor machinery which powered the remaining two pairs of underdraft stones. One set of stones consisted of 4 foot diameter French burrs, complete with iron spindles and stone nuts, originally worked by a 5 foot 6 inch wooden clasp-arm great spur wheel. At its hub an all wood flanged pulley was said to have driven a single 'master' governor. The tower's base diameter measured 15 feet 3 inches, while the wall thickness was 3 feet, decreasing as it ascended to about 2 feet at dust floor level, the diameter here being 14 feet.

During the post war years the tower was internally dismantled, perhaps for safety reasons, because of its proximity to the nearby public right of way. One wonders why the whole building was not demolished, but thankfully the shell was spared, proving much later to be an investment to an enterprising owner. Alterations began during the spring or summer of 1981. Brackley builders Francis J. Ayres and Co. erected two large adjoining extensions either side of the tower in a style reminiscent of the traditional English barn. The two-storey additions comprised a main house and an annex.

By early 1982 the former shell had been transformed into not just a house conversion but a superb four bedroom luxury home with two bathrooms, two reception rooms, a studio, games room and heated swimming pool. The tower itself remains the central point of the creation, with red brick crenellations topping the stone work. Within, the floors are accessible via a cast iron spiral staircase, and the windows throughout are double glazed. As well as permitting access to the roof, a balcony at the second floor affords a splendid view of the surrounding countryside, including the watermill pond and part of the village.

Many molinologists, including the author, have often expressed reservations about derelict mills being gutted and converted into dwellings, but Sulgrave tower mill is a fine example of an empty shell redeveloped into a splendid home while still retaining much of its originality. In 1988 the property was valued at well over a quarter of a million pounds.

TANSOR TOWER MILL

The shell of Tansor's windmill can be found within the grounds of Tansor Court. This small country mansion, part of which is believed to have been a rectory, is complemented by fine gardens, stables and the tower mill. At the present time the structure stands unused, and is more of a large garden ornament encircled by a flower bed. It is four storeys in height and covered by a flat roof. The top of the tower has been edged with battlements, but for all of its forlorn appearance the building is kept in a preserved state.

The ground, first and second floors are built of ironstone, but its third storey is constructed of red brick, possibly implying that the mill was heightened at some time during its early life - although this is purely conjecture. Much of the cement rendering remains intact, and glazing has been added to some window ways. As with most tower mills there are two opposing ground floor doorways, and this mill has two window ways per floor. The wall thickness at the base is between 2 and 2 $1/_2$ feet, and seems to be the same at the top.

Although bare of any equipment and all flooring, the tower still possesses its curb anchor irons which now hang vertically. Outside, leaning against the structure, are three peak stones, one of them of noticeable thickness. Nothing was kept in the old mill during my visit of May 1980, which perhaps was understandable as, when viewing the inside, I was all too aware of the foul smell of dampness and bird droppings. At that time it was the gardener, Mr Squares, who cared for most of the estate, with the assistance of Mr Bill Rootham, then in his eighties and still enjoying bell ringing at the village church. Both gentlemen provided much information.

During its working days Tansor mill's four sails — two common and two double shuttered patent — took power to two pairs of millstones. These are claimed to have been French burrs, but only Derbyshire peaks were found at the site. A single wooden lever for adjusting the stones featured upon the stone floor, as did a master governor. All the overdrift machinery was of wooden construction, including the octagonal upright shaft, the stone nuts and the great spur wheel which bore an inner ring of teeth, supposedly for driving a dressing machine.

The ground floor was not the place for a tall man. From the ground to the principal beams it measured only 6 feet. The whole thing was crowned with an ogee cap, and winded by means of a fantail. An arrangement typical of the Cambridgeshire style made up the fan cradle. The eight vanes were mounted high above a short stage, and the diagonal supports were bolted to the sides of the cap. All in all the mill would have completed the scene of rural tranquillity. Visible from the main road between Oundle and Peterborough (now the A605) it must have made a fine sight with its white-painted sweeps rotating in a clockwise direction. A good view of the mill is still possible from the gardens of a one-time public house, 'The White Horse', now privately owned and situated not far from the old bakery.

The mill is not depicted on the 1779 county map and is absent from the survey

Tansor tower mill during the pre-war years as seen from the gardens of 'The White Horse' public house. [Photo: Maurice and Joyce Palmer]

maps of 1824 and 1835. It is, however, referred to in Pigot's directory of 1841 along with Thomas Sawford as miller. He is mentioned in Kelly's 1847 directory, but in Slater's directory of 1850 he seems to have been mistakenly recorded as 'Lawford'. A few years later in 1854, Tansor mill was being run by William Sawford (possibly Thomas's son), who continued milling for many years as well as being involved in other businesses. Mr Sawford was indeed a busy man. Apart from the mill he ran the bakery, a farm, and eventually found time to act as landlord at 'The White Horse'.

Between 1885 and 1890 Mr Alfred Brown had superseded Mr Sawford in all of his activities. The name Sawford does not appear in any further directories, but it is clear that Mr Brown had taken over not just the mill and bakery, but also the 'White Horse'.

As with any wind or water mill, repairs were commonplace, often undertaken by the miller himself, and sometimes by outside specialists. In 1889 the need for some renovation work arose, and for this a carpenter and joiner was employed. The sails especially needed attention. Whether repaired or replaced the cost of the work was

Tansor mill in June 1935 from the grounds of Tansor Court. [Photo: Donald W. Muggeridge]

Tansor mill: an empty shell with crenellated top in 1980. [Photo: The author]

about £400. Unfortunately, some time later it was discovered the carpenter had not allowed for any weathering on the sweeps, and the mill's performance suffered greatly. Not long afterwards, during the early to mid 1890s, Tansor tower mill ceased work. Towards the end of its life the mill had been producing flour solely for the bakery. This, and only this, kept the windmill working, as was realized with some concern by the miller.

Alfred Brown continued with his other duties. In the 1898 directory he is recorded as a 'Baker and Beer retailer'. It was recalled by Bill Rootham that Mr Brown was later joined at the bakery by his son who also eventually took over the pub. Exactly when is unknown, but by 1924 the bakery had passed to George Henry Pollard while as late as 1931 Alfred Brown (possibly junior) could still be found at 'The White Horse'. The owner of Tansor Court at this time was Mrs Maude Mills.

During the 1930s it was proposed to convert the windmill into a water tower. Pumping equipment would supply the gardens with water drawn from the nearby River Nene. Two large water storage tanks were installed at the top of the mill. To accommodate them the sails, windshaft, brake wheel and wallower had to be removed. Once the tanks and the pumps were in place the cap was made weatherproof around the area where the windshaft would have protruded. Externally its appearance differed little, apart from the loss of its sails; even the fan cradle was left in place.

In July 1932 Tansor mill was pictured by the artist Karl S. Wood. Another noted visitor, Donald W. Muggeridge, one of the old school of molinologists, photographed the mill in June 1935. By this time it still possessed a great deal of its machinery and its stones, although the ladders above the first floor had been removed, and generally its condition was bad. Some years later, in the mid-fifties, the then owner of Tansor Court, Mr Walter Garner, arranged for the structure to undergo a further alteration.

It seems obvious that its function as a water tower was now no longer required, but thankfully Mr Garner decided against having the old mill totally demolished. Instead the tower would be gutted, leaving it for use perhaps as a store. The firm chosen for the work was Frank Coles, builders of Wansford. Mr Garner arranged to meet Mr Coles on the site, and the builder later recalled (in a letter to Henry Wozniak): '… that the mill was in reasonably good condition, but the top [perhaps referring to the cap] was mainly missing.' Mr Coles also remembered wooden 'drive wheels' (great spur wheel and stone nuts) and the (upright) 'shaft' which he described as being 'balanced on large ball-bearings at the bottom'. The gear was removed along with the two large water tanks, and later on the flooring. Mr Garner then asked for the cap to be removed, which Mr Coles recalled as 'decayed and dangerous'. Once accomplished, the top was levelled off and crenellated with a course of concrete blocks. Any salvaged material was left on the site.

A photograph of the complete mill can be found at the Northamptonshire Record Office at Delapre Abbey. The view shows the tower mill with sails forming a backdrop for children in Edwardian costume. A more detailed picture appears in the 1910 edition (volume 3) of *Country House* — once again, complete with sails but lacking its fan. Currently held in the Northampton Central Library is J. A. Perrin's fine portrait of Tansor Mill painted in 1915.

My thanks go to Mr Maurice Newns of Tansor, and once again to Henry Wozniak.

WELDON POST MILL

Just outside Corby lies Weldon, home of an industrial estate and a number of quarries. The village itself retains a certain charm even though it has swelled somewhat in recent years. Many elderly stone-built cottages survive within the parish, but sadly the old post mill which once dominated the skyline has long gone. Standing in a field beside the Larratt Road the old post mill bore an extremely primitive look with its square horizontally boarded buck, vertically boarded pitched roof and its open trestle. The four clockwise sails consisted of two types, patent and common sweeps, winded by a long, curving tailpole which added to its ancient appearance. In this case, however, appearances were deceptive, for this is not the windmill marked on the 1779 or 1824 maps which was an earlier example thought to have been run by Corby man Philip Hinkley.

The Weldon post mill formerly stood at Wing in Rutland, to the south-east of the village very close to another post mill on the opposite side of the Glaston road. Both of these mills were standing in 1819 when they were owned by Robert Peach of Whissendine. One of them was described in *The Stamford Mercury* in April of that year as '... the best mill in the county of Rutland'. The notice offering the two windmills for sale claimed that this mill was 'new erected', but it would seem that no sale was made, for ten years later both mills were offered by Mrs Peach (who might have become widowed by that time). By now both mills were 'old established, well built post mills' (and all this by 1829!). As well as Mrs Peach, prospective purchasers were to contact the Oakham baker, Mr Almond.

These mills are known to have contained two stone sets: one French and the other peak. A bunt machine was also mentioned, together with the fact that both of the mills had large roundhouses. Another sale notice appeared in the *Mercury* in September 1838 when one of the windmills, by now in the occupation of Joseph Slater, was offered with the understanding that it would be removed from 'the premises'. The sale was to take place at The Exeter Arms inn on 17 September, but this seems to have been another failure because a further advertisement appeared in the newspaper on 25 January 1839. Eventually the post mill was sold to Philip Hinkley. Reference to one 'Mr Inckles' having removed the windmill appears to be a mistaken rendering of Hinkley. The mill was dismantled, transported and later re-erected at Little Weldon (as the village was formerly known). One major difference from the mill in the original site was the omission of the roundhouse.

Meanwhile Mr Slater, along with John Bradshaw, continued to run the remaining Wing post mill. Long after its companion had been taken away people would ask the reason why. The answer was always that 'there was not enough wind for both mills.'

It was in the trade directory of 1847 that William Hinkley was listed as Little Weldon's miller, and the census of 1851 suggests that his trade had brought him prosperity. As well as his wife Elizabeth and four children, the family employed a 14-year-old servant girl. All in all the Hinkleys ran the post mill for 17 years until

The rustic Little Weldon post mill which survived until it was blown down on Boxing Day 1915. Note that a figure to the left of Mr Hunt has been 'blanked' out from the photograph. [Photo: F.C.A. Colyer]

February 1856 when a sale notice appeared in *The Stamford Mercury* offering the windmill for sale by auction, this time at the King's Arms, Little Weldon. It was purchased by John Hunt from Catworth in Huntingdonshire, and thereafter became known in the district as 'Hunt's Mill'. This tradition continued after 1860 when the building had passed to Hunt's son, also John, who is thought to have subsequently acquired a portable steam engine to provide power during windless days. Mr Hunt also drew help from a pony which was hitched to the tailpole for winding when the need arose. When it died in 1870 the owner had it buried beneath the windmill.

John Hunt the younger married Jane Richardson, the daughter of a village carpenter. The couple soon settled into a pretty cottage (now Primrose Cottage) in 1882. It is near to the main Corby road in Water Lane, once known as Marches Hill, and is a fair walk from Larratt Road. The Hunts were well respected, and in addition to his windmill Mr Hunt ran a successful farm. Later he came to own several in the parish. He was a man of strict principles, and never smoked or drank — but he

One of the few remains of Weldon post mill in 1981 — in this case, possibly a sack hoist gear.
[Photo: The author]

allowed himself the pleasure of fathering six children.

Two men were employed by the Hunts on occasions, to help work the windmill — Mr Burdett and William Farren. The latter was a real character, and said to have been the strongest man in Weldon, able to lift an 18 stone sack of wheat onto his shoulders with ease. He was also a dedicated bell-ringer and would often abandon his work to run the quarter of a mile to the Church, ring the 8 p.m. curfew, then run back.

The harvest was a busy time in the miller's calendar, and Little Weldon was no

Weldon's stone nut in 1981, less its wooden teeth. Since then it has sadly disintegrated.
[Photo: The author]

Little Weldon post mill from Water Lane early this century. The mill is without its sail frames.
[Photo: Northampton Record Office]

exception, sometimes working all day and through the night. The windmill also proved to be popular with the village's poor, as many of them would salvage stray remnants of corn, later to be ground at the mill.

One can appreciate how difficult and dangerous it must have been for the miller during those nights in a hot, cramped space with only the light of an oil-lamp or a candle to see by. He would have to remain forever alert to avoid becoming caught by the mechanism, and there was always the risk of fire. Whenever high winds were blowing, Mr Hunt made it a policy to be present at the mill in order to reduce the chance of tail-winding.

In 1903, at the age of 63, John Hunt died and, as was expected, the windmill passed to his sons. Although Joshua's name appears in the directory of 1906 it is known that he was helped in his work by his brothers. For a while they were assisted by a Mr Loveday, but generally the Hunts found greater rewards in farming than in the declining trade of windmilling. The post mill was soon abandoned and the sail frames removed to prevent it from turning. It was in this condition that the decaying windmill was struck by lightning during the summer of 1913, but this did not account for its destruction. The wooden building continued to defy the elements until it was eventually overpowered by a gale, and it crashed to the ground on the evening of

Boxing Day 1915. The remains were soon cleared away, and today the site of the post mill is little more than waste land.

Sadly there are no more Hinkleys or Hunts in the village, but a grand-daughter of John Hunt, Miss Florence C. A. Colyer now lives in Primrose Cottage. Until recently she was a church councillor and an active member of the W.I. Florence takes a great interest in the village's history, and some years ago contributed a feature on her grandfather's windmill to the local historical magazine *Weldon in the Woods*. In the article Mrs Colyer gave an eyewitness account of the lightning strike of 1913. 'It was very spectacular; like a ball of fire had hit the windmill.'

The stones were said to have survived, but this seems to be based on hearsay, and at this point no definite evidence can be found to confirm the rumour. Happily a number of relics from the building do survive and are held by Miss Colyer. These include some timbers in the garden (none of which can readily be identified), together with a wooden stone nut and an iron spur gear. The stone nut has a diameter of 15 inches and consists of 17 applewood cogs linked by 17 bolts which clamp the cogs in place. Over the years the weather has taken its toll, causing the centre to soften and, as a result, the teeth of the cogs have long ago broken away just leaving the shanks. The iron spur gear has a diameter of 24 inches, boasts 51 teeth, and is believed to have been part of the sack hoist. At the centre of the wheel a spiked extension joined it to a wooden shaft. During my recent visit to Weldon, Miss Colyer presented me with the spur gear in an effort to preserve something of the mill. (Unfortunately, my attempt to load the gear into my car caused the wheel and the shaft to separate for the first time in some 170 years.) Also in Miss Colyer's possession is the large nine-inch-long key to the mill which is kept for sentimental reasons.

WOOTTON TOWER MILL

Since the thirteenth century there has been a windmill at Wootton. Two windmills are known to have stood within the grounds of Wootton Manor in 1283. Much later in 1779 a windmill is shown on Eyre and Jefferys' map of the county. The mill, a post mill, was the property of Mr George Travell and survived until late one Thursday evening during October 1813 when a violent storm sent the old wooden structure crashing to the ground. The miller, his wife and a second lady must have been in the mill, or in the vicinity, for it was recorded that they had 'just time enough to leave it before it fell'. All three escaped without serious injury.

The post mill had stood on a slight mound, and it was on this very site (possibly even on the former mill's roundhouse foundations) that Mr Travell erected a replacement tower mill between 1815 and 1820. The new tower mill was constructed

Wootton tower mill in its heyday, showing the bowsprit to advantage.
[Photo: F. Coles]

Wootton mill in working condition. Although 'working with the aid of steam' no engine shed or pulley can be seen.
[Photo: F. Coles]

of red brick and was five storeys high (including a basement) and stood 40 feet high at its cap. The base diameter measured 21 feet, and at the curb 10 feet. Ground floor walls were 2 feet thick and, as with almost all windmills, there were two doorways opposite each other. At the western doorway was a wooden loading platform with stone steps. The door itself was of the double door type found in stables. Eight windows were claimed to be of varying sizes but, no doubt, as in many mills, lighting must have been a constant problem, especially during winter months.

Inside the basement the upper floor is supported by a single central brick pier. Examination of the foundations reveals they are of ironstone, and this reinforces the theory that the tower mill was built on the remains of the former post mill roundhouse. The basement was used as a storeroom, while from the ground floor a dressing machine and a single governor could be seen, so it is possible the mill was overdriven as there is no record of any other machinery at this level. The stones, sets of peaks and French burrs, may have been situated on the first floor if this is so. Above them was the wooden-framed dome cap with its decorative petticoat and an eight-bladed fantail. Winding could also be accomplished by use of a luffing wheel located at the rear of the fanstage.

Wootton Tower Mill originally formed part of an estate owned by Mr William Oliver Harris who lived at Wootton Hall. The miller in 1847 had been Mr William

Frank C. Gill's 1923 drawing of Wootton mill entitled 'Wootton Mill Reconstructed'. There is no evidence of a stage ever having existed at this mill. [Reproduced with the permission of R.C. Gill]

Marriott who was still working the windmill in 1874. Five years later a report appeared in *The Miller* describing the dissolution of the partnership between millers Mr Marriott and Mr Webb at Wootton. Around 1894 Messrs Winkles and Pearson are listed at the mill, but by 1903 Thomas Winkles was conducting the business in his name only. Thomas's nephew, Mr D. W. Winkles, told me in 1981 that the Winkles family originated in Holland, and possibly worked at the Long Buckby watermill for a short while. After acquiring Wootton mill, Thomas replaced the original sails with four single-shuttered anti-clockwise patent sweeps which were purchased from the tower mill at Silverstone (see page 122). Installing the secondhand sails fell to Thomas and his brother, father of Mr D. W. Winkles. Afterwards it was found necessary to strengthen them with rigging. A bowsprit was mounted forward of the striking gear via brackets, seemingly fitted to the edge of the canister. From the tip of the bowsprit, tensioned cables supported the sails, and similar cables (or chains as has been claimed) were fixed at mid-point from one sweep to another. In his book *In Search of English Windmills*, Stanley Freese describes Wootton's bowsprit arrangement as being 'similar to that on Stanningfield mill [Suffolk post mill] but smaller.' However, in a print of the mill by H. W. Keyte, which appeared in the *Northampton County Magazine* of 1928, the bowsprit is shown to be offset and fixed to one of the sail stocks beside the canister. With respect to Mr Keyte, his drawing is attractive but basic, and one should not place too much faith in its technical accuracy.

Prior to legislation restricting the amount of feed produced by wind and watermills

Wootton mill in 1947 with two millstones still in evidence. [Photo: Donald W. Muggeridge]

for human consumption, Wootton Mill ground wheat, oats and barley. For maximum effort, Mr Winkles installed a portable steam engine in an outbuilding. (This itself is a curious fact as every photograph the author has seen of the mill, whether working or derelict, has shown it to be very isolated, with no external pulley visible.) The mill is

As Wootton mill appeared in 1980. Recently the stump has become part of a newly built house. [Photo: The author]

Wootton mill as it appears today. [Photo: The author]

listed as working as late as 1920 by steam power, but it is generally accepted that it ceased work at the outbreak of the Great War. One contributing factor to the windmill's closure may have been an accident involving the steam engine which exploded in the presence of the miller. Mr Winkles suffered severe injuries to his leg and walked with a limp thereafter.

During the 1920s the tower mill was owned by Mrs Hooley, but it soon fell into disrepair and it was in this state that it was seen by Stanley Freese in 1929. Freese reported that the mill still carried its sails and cable connections, but seemed to be in a very dilapidated state with much debris around the site. Some years later, possibly 1935, the tower mill underwent a conversion which included the extraction of all machinery and the removal of the cap. The sails had already been taken down for safety reasons, and the now empty tower was given a flat roof. This conflicts with G. N. Shann's notes which claimed that the mill had been 'demolished'.

Mr D. W. Winkles remembers that his father, who had assisted with the fitting of the sails 30 years before, investigated the possibilities of modifying the tower into a dwelling. However, the building was eventually altered to become a water tower. By this time the structure was standing alone, and only two millstones — one peak and one French — remained outside, while the mill's flat roof had been edged with iron railings.

The next stage in this windmill's varied life came during the Second World War. By 1940 the threat of invasion and airborne landings seemed very real, and recently formed Home Guard units made use of any tall buildings to serve as lookout posts. With its flat roof and railings, Wootton tower mill provided local defenders with an excellent observation platform. A number of county mills were used for this purpose, including Barby, Blakesley, Braunston and Silverstone, and like these mills Wootton tower mill survived the war, but its greatest threat came from peacetime redevelopment.

In the early fifties the tower and part of the adjoining land was purchased by Mr Norman Bell, and his brother Dennis, owner of Bell Motors. Rather than have the tower demolished, the brothers employed builders Ray and Peter Clements to truncate the mill to two storeys in height. A tiled octagonal roof was added, finished off with a large weather vane, and in 1953 the conversion was put up for sale. The buyer, Mr F. Coles, moved into an adjacent house recently constructed by Dennis Bell. Norman Bell did not live to see the growth of the housing estate built on the mill fields.

In 1981 the writer spent an enjoyable evening in the company of Mr and Mrs Coles which included an inspection of the truncation. At that time the stump was being used by the Coles's teenage son as a 'disco den' with lighting equipment and amplifiers in storage. The upper storeys had been painted in bright colours, while the basement was untouched and empty. At this level it was possible to see the difference in construction of the earlier building. Outside in the garden between the mill and the house were two millstones set up as ornaments, the final remnants of its windmill days. Since then a further change has taken place with the erection of a new house in about 1985 which incorporates the truncated tower. Care has been taken to match the brickwork as well as the roof tiles.

PART II

Windmills in the Soke of Peterborough

BARNACK POST MILL

At the turn of the century only two post mills were to be found within the Soke of Peterborough. One was in the Fengate district of Peterborough, and the second was located in the western part of the Soke, less than a quarter of a mile west of the village of Barnack which already played host to a large tower mill. The small post mill was easily visible from the stone-built tower, but far from being overshadowed by it the wooden windmill displayed a number of interesting features that made it stand out, including its sails and roundhouse.

In other respects, too, the mill differed from many of its kind found throughout Northamptonshire and neighbouring Huntingdonshire, and although some characteristics were uniform with the other mills, Barnack remained the exception.

Typically, the buck was horizontally boarded, but the breast, sides and the curved

Barnack post mill showing the curious 'roundhouse roof'. Note also the box-type protrusion at the side of the body below the roof. This is said to have been a vent for a grain cleaner installed within the mill.
[Photo: Peterborough Museum and Art Gallery]

144

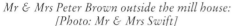

Mr & Mrs Peter Brown outside the mill house:
[Photo: Mr & Mrs Swift]

The mill house today.
[Photo: Nigel Moon]

roof were clad in extremely narrow planks, while the much wider boards were employed at the rear of the mill. A large wide ladder led up to double doors, and beneath these a well-worn tailpole passed through the upper centre of the steps, allowing the mill to be manually levered to face the wind. The supporting structure, or trestle, of the post mill was enclosed within a stone-built roundhouse, described by Rex Wailes in 1950 as being of 'beehive shape'. This was roofed by the skirt of the mill body which bulged at the base of the sides and breast to accommodate the skirt. This would have given the impression that, during winding, the roundhouse 'roof' would have been seen to revolve with the buck. The windmill was equipped with four clockwise turning spring sails which were adjusted by the levers near the tip of each sweep, while the actual spring mechanism was housed in rectangular boxes positioned at the centre of each whip. More often than not, spring sails were mounted in pairs with the second set of sweeps comprising common sails, as with Rushden smock mill (see page 115) which employed an identical spring system, or Easton-on-the-Hill tower mill (see page 58), but of course there were exceptions to this rule.

No windmills appear on Eyre and Jefferys' map of 1779 (actually surveyed by Thomas Eyre in 1779 and revised by Thomas Jefferys in 1791) at 'Barnoak', but two were illustrated in A. Bryant's county map of 1824-26 and the 'First Edition' Ordnance Survey map of 1824, including the site of the present tower mill (claimed to have been built in 1840). However, an earlier reference is to be found in *The Stamford Mercury* of 7 November 1806, when the post mill was offered for sale by Leonard Thorpe of Barnack, and Duddington man, William Cunnington, who later constructed the tower mill at Kings Cliffe (see page 80). It was reported to be 'an exceedingly good post windmill with two pairs of stones, a flour machine and a flour mill.' The advertisement went on to say that the structure stood upon half an acre of freehold land and enjoyed good business. It seems that the owners were quite willing to allow the buyer to dismantle the windmill and transport it to another site if necessary.

The new owner, Thomas Leake, was content to work the mill without resorting to such actions, and by the summer of 1815 the building, said to be in an excellent condition, was put up for auction. By 1838 the post mill was being run by the Gilbert

One of a number of sail whips found recently at the site of Barnack post mill.
[Photo: Nigel Moon]

family, the *Mercury* for June of that year claimed Mrs Gilbert was in charge. Some years later in 1847 Mr W. Gilbert was listed in the trade directory as the miller.

A further entry of 1854 indicated that Mr Gilbert was still at work, but by the late 1860s he had been succeeded by the Brown family. Mr J. Brown was listed in the 1869 directory, and soon afterwards Peter Brown, Barnack post mill's last miller, had taken charge.

The Brown family were well established in the milling trade, having formerly worked the post mill at Great Easton, and possibly the tower mill at Medbourne, both in Leicestershire. Peter's brother, Mark, is known to have run one of the Crowland post mills, and his son later described in a diary a train journey across the Fens to see 'Uncle Peter's mill at Barnack'. Peter Brown continued operating the windmill, and the bakery adjoining the millhouse, until his death on 12 December 1910 aged 75. Not long afterwards the post mill, millhouse and the surrounding land were sold for approximately £250 to a local farmer, Steven Taylor, who eventually rented out the house and bakery to a Mr Wallace. The latter became known as 'The Midnight Baker' which arose from his dislike of waking early to bake. This often meant that his deliveries took place at midnight, which understandably proved unpopular. As a result the business failed to prosper. Wallace died during the 1920s, and the property subsequently passed to the parents of the wife of the current owner of the millhouse. The post mill sadly no longer exists, having been demolished in 1916. Whether it ever worked again after 1910 is not known, but by 1913 neither of the two Barnack windmills were operating.

Another version of the windmill's destruction is documented within the notes of Herbert E. S. Simmons (new held by the Science Museum Library in London) where it is stated that the structure succumbed to high winds sometime between 1905 and 1906, but the description of the mill is inconsistent with other reports. The contributor, a Mr Cobbin, claims the post mill had an open trestle and four common sails. This is clearly an error, and probably refers to another mill yet to be identified.

Recently the author's friend, Nigel Moon (who helped with much of this section) explored the site, and he was surprised to find that little had changed. The mill house and grounds remained much as they did from the time of the windmill, unlike so many other former mill sites. Also discovered were pieces of a French burr stone and a number of sail whips stored within an outbuilding. Some of the whips were clearly made for shuttered sails but the design of the remainder suggested they were for common sweeps.

Basically these timbers differed from the shuttered examples by having a greater number of mortices which once accepted the sail bars. If this is so, one might assume that these sails pre-dated the springs seen in the accompanying photographs. The fact that they have survived to this day gives one cause to wonder what other treasures are to be found around the county. Another reminder of the windmill is provided by the village pub, where the author and a friend were only too grateful to refresh themselves after scrambling about in the tower mill. It is aptly named 'The Millstone'.

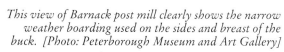

This view of Barnack post mill clearly shows the narrow weather boarding used on the sides and breast of the buck. [Photo: Peterborough Museum and Art Gallery]

147

BARNACK TOWER MILL

Anyone travelling on the A1 between Stamford and Peterborough may catch a distant glimpse of the handsome tower mill at Barnack, with its shining aluminium cap and four sail stocks. Visible over a large distance across flat countryside, it stands half a mile west of the village at 'Windmill Farm' in a very picturesque rural setting which would have easily made Barnack Mill the best preserved of all Northamptonshire windmills. Sadly, when the county boundaries were revised in 1965, the Soke of Peterborough was amalgamated with Huntingdonshire, and then, in 1974, with the county of Cambridgeshire. Because it was originally a Northamptonshire mill it has been included (as with other Soke windmills) in this book.

The tower mill is owned by the Marquis of Exeter and the Burghley Estate Trust,

Barnack tower mill in 1935 with a full complement of stocks and whips.
[Photo: Donald Muggeridge]

The mill in 1950 with one broken whip.
[Photo: H. Meyer collection via A.C. Smith]

In 1972 boasting its replacement cap.
[Photo: A.C. Smith]

and is kept under the watchful eye of Mr Kenneth Isaac Woolley who lives at the adjacent farmhouse. He and his family are justly pround of the limestone tower rising five storeys to its relatively recently replaced cap. As well as the four stocks and whips the mill retains its fan cradle. Damage to one of the whips was noticed in 1981 by the author (this can be traced back to 1972 in Arthur C. Smith's *Windmills in Huntingdon and Peterborough* where a photograph shows the uppermost whip broken off level with the end of the stock.) Upon my visit of January 1989 I was surprised to find yet another whip had suffered the same fate. The subject was raised with Mr Woolley, who informed me that by 1981/82 the whip, which overhung the drive to the house, was drooping and threatening to fall, perhaps on a passing vehicle. Unable to repair the damage, Mr Woolley resorted to other means. With the aid of a fishing rod, a line was cast over the sagging whip, and to the end of the line a rope was tied then hauled over. Both ends of the rope were pulled, and with a little help the whip snapped, shattering on impact. If this is typical of the state of decay in the remaining stocks and whips then obviously it should give cause for concern.

Within the tower, beginning at the very top, the replacement cap is wooden-ribbed complete with a doorway to the fan stage. Many of the drive gears from the absent fantail are stored upon the dust floor. Seven out of eight centering wheels remain attached to the headframe where one of the forward timbers bears the carving 'JEE 1X7V' (although it could be 187-). The large wooden clasp arm brake wheel has a

149

Cap, fantail (without vanes) and cradle of Barnack tower mill.
[Photo: The author]

Clasp-arm brake wheel with a ring of iron teeth. The brake shoe can also be seen.
[Photo: Steve Johnson]

The great spur wheel supported by a heavy 'H' frame. [Photo: The author]

Another row of teeth above the spur wheel powers two drive shafts, both completely different in construction. [Photo: The author]

An overdriven stone assembly with the hopper support — the horse — sitting on top of the vat.
[Photo: The author]

circle of the cast iron teeth. It was claimed by the late Rex Wailes that originally the brake wheel would have had sections of teeth instead of the current single casting. Wailes also mentioned in his *Transactions of the Newcomen Society*, 'Windmills of Cambridgeshire', that Barnack's windshaft has the largest in the area, being 22 inches in diameter at the brake wheel, tapering to 20 inches at its tail end. Forward of the brake wheel, the windshaft can best be described as a 'box-like' fitting, strengthened with iron clamps. Beyond that, an iron canister or poll-end completes the assembly. Engaging the brake wheel a solid cast iron wallower is fixed to a wooden octagonal upright shaft that passes through the dust (fourth) floor. One of the errors of the partial reinstatement is that the flooring has been replaced right up to the upright shaft, fixing it so tightly that it could never revolve. The internal diameter at this level is 13 feet 10 inches, while the wall thickness is 1 foot 7 inches.

Typical throughout this mill are the white plastered walls and the two pairs of opposing window ways to each floor. However, in most cases the north-western and south-eastern windows have been bricked up, probably as a result of the Victorian window tax. Obviously these alterations were carried out in the windmill's early days,

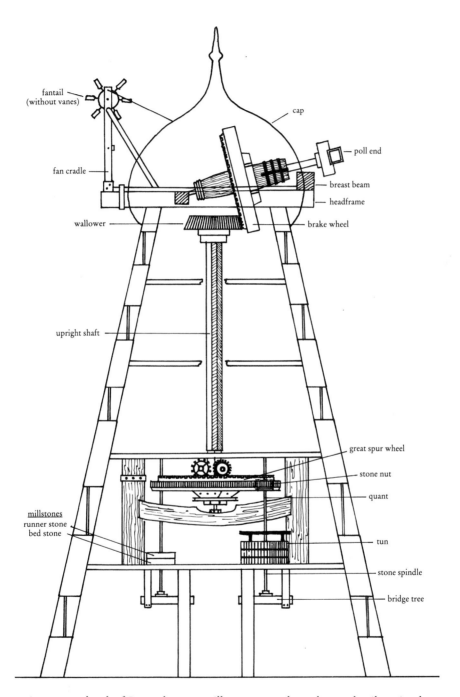

fantail
(without vanes)

cap

poll end

fan cradle

breast beam

headframe

wallower

brake wheel

upright shaft

great spur wheel

stone nut

quant

millstones
runner stone
bed stone

tun

stone spindle

bridge tree

A cutaway sketch of Barnack tower mill — not to scale, and some details omitted.

as many pieces of equipment have been installed in their place, such as the wooden pulley measuring 1 foot 10 inches in diameter. This may be part of the sack hoist, but the only evidence for this claim is the fact that it is in line with the trap doors found on every floor. On the third floor, where the diameter is 16 feet 1 inch, the sealed south-eastern window is hidden behind a wooden meal chute. Excluding the chute and the presence of the upright shaft, this floor is relatively bare. Equally sparse is the second floor which used to be the bin floor, except now there are no bins! Apart from the ever present upright shaft, only a single diagonal metal strut is to be seen, although its purpose is unknown. The diameter of this floor is 18 feet 4 inches, and beneath here is the stone floor where the mill seems to spring to life again in a melee of gears and stones. Unfortunately, none is capable of working. Dominating this floor is the wooden clasp-arm great spur wheel which is set low over the stones, and at 10 feet in diameter is said to be the largest in the area. Two timber posts and a sagging crossbeam bear its weight, and three wooden stone nuts are fixed to iron quants which in turn are attached to the millstones.

When writing of this mill in September 1961, Rex Wailes suggested the possibility that much of the machinery may have come from a watermill, or was constructed by a millwright with only watermill experience, making Barnack a unique windmill.

Continuing with the description of the stone floor: of the stones themselves two pairs are encased in vats (also known as 'tuns'), while a third set is without. This pair, situated at the eastern point measures 4 feet 6 inches in diameter. Much smaller is the western stone set, the wooden tun being calculated at 4 feet 8 inches. Both this and the southern vat are sporting horses, but hoppers and other pieces of feeding equipment are absent. The remaining machinery comprises two auxiliary drive systems; one consisting of a small vertically positioned wooden spur gear which is connected to a wooden pulley located on the north-west wall, rather uncomfortably above the ground floor ladder. A matter of feet to the right (with the first floor doorway in between) is a four-spoked gear driven via a smaller cog wheel engaging the great spur wheel. It seems likely the wall-pulley drove a dresser, while the spoked gear powered the sack hoist. (I repeat the claim made when referring to the dust floor pulley — my only evidence being the relation of these to the sack traps.)

The light from two windows allowed the floor to be measured with ease, this being 20 feet 9 inches in diameter. Instead of sealed windows there are doors, one (previously mentioned) at the north-west point is still used while its opposite is bricked up. In this the ground floor is unique, as it is the only level where apertures have not been altered, and two doorways and two windows give access and light respectively. Three large square timber posts support the stone floor as well as the three bridge trees, but sadly no trace of the single master governor, or the rest of the tentering gear could be found. The ground floor itself is paved and has a diameter of 21 feet 6 inches and a wall thickness measuring 2 feet 8 inches. Should anybody be interested after this lengthy collection of calculations, the doors work out at 6 feet 2 inches by 3 feet 5 inches.

It is generally accepted that Barnack tower mill was built in 1840, although Mr John Martin advertised in *The Stamford Mercury* of 22 November 1839 requesting the services of a journeyman miller. Unable to fill the post, Mr Martin repeated the advertisement during the following March. By November 1840, John Martin junior, who also worked at the windmill, was declared bankrupt, although his creditors were

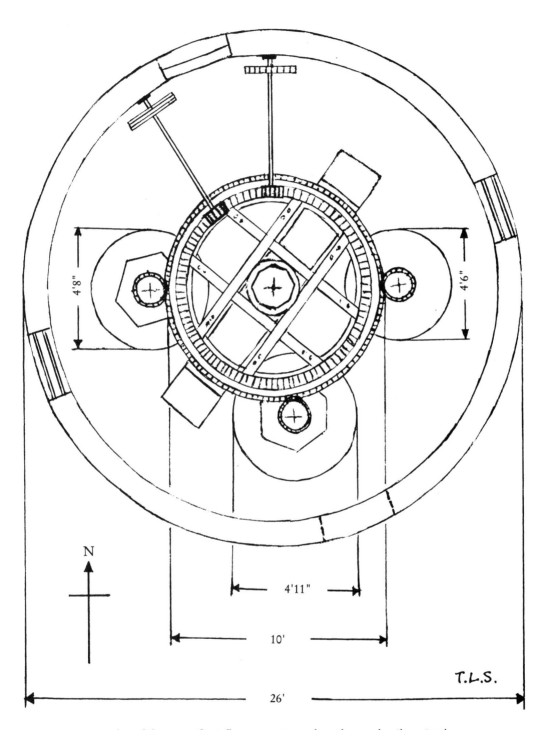

N

4'8"

4'6"

4'11"

10'

26'

T.L.S.

A plan of the stone (first) floor — not to scale and some details omitted.

later to receive payment of ten shillings in the pound. This proved to be only the beginning of further misfortune for Martin jun. In the early days of August 1846 a violent storm hit Barnack around noon on a Sunday. Two of the mill's four patent sails were torn off and totally destroyed. Plagued by bad luck, John Martin jun. was given notice to quit in January 1847. The mill was put up for auction along with the house and bakery. Further details could be obtained from Mr Martin sen.

In about 1850 one Mr W. Pentelow was the miller, and by 1864 it had passed to Mr Charles Sanderson. At some uncertain time during the nineteenth century, both the post mill and the tower mill were owned by a Mr Turner, but throughout the latter part of the mill's working life it was Mr Sanderson who conducted operations and carried out repairs. Further damage to the mill was suffered in March 1895 when a gale carried away the fantail, and for a short while there was a fear of 'tail winding'. In time the fantail was replaced and the tower remained in Charles's care through the turn of the century. Alfred Sanderson briefly followed, but by 1906 the Sandersons had been succeeded by Mr Henry Stokes, Barnack's last miller. The windmill seems to have ceased work in 1913 according to Henry's son Gus Stokes, 86 years old in 1989. By the early 1920s it had become derelict, and although remaining so throughout the early thirties, the mill stayed in an essentially sound condition. By this time the four patent sweeps had been removed along with the fantail, but the cap, fan cradle, sail stocks and whips were left intact.

During its decadence the mill was examined by various enthusiasts and societies, including Rex Wailes, Herbert E. S. Simmons and Donald W. Muggeridge. Reports and general information concerning the mill was collated, and in 1959 an appeal for funds to renovate the mill was launched by the Northamptonshire branch of the Council for the Preservation of Rural England, the 'Men of Stones' from Stamford and the Peterborough Society. The initial target sum was £650, but this subsequently had to be raised to £900. The Marquis of Exeter, who by then owned the mill, contributed £150, and by December 1960 £700 of the total required had been raised. Work on the mill started in 1961, principally concerned with making it weatherproof at first. The cap's wooden frame was rebuilt and clad with aluminium, and windows and doors were replaced. R. Thompson & Son, the millwrights of Alford, Lincolnshire, undertook much of the work.

In 1982 Mr Woolley investigated on behalf of the Trust the cost of a total restoration. A firm of millwrights are said to have quoted £100,000 for a complete job, and £60,000 to 'tidy up' and make it weatherproof. Even though it is a Grade 1 listed building, Barnack tower mill and the Burghley Estate Trustees can only hope that such funds will one day become available.

CASTOR TOWER MILL

Both of the Castor mills still exist and are easily seen from the footpath that leads down from 'Mill Lane' alongside the River Nene to Alwalton. Now converted, the large watermill makes a fine residence, still retaining its outward appearance, and an atmosphere captured in sound as the river roars through the mill race. The windmill, by contrast, is nothing more than an empty tower fenced off in a nearby field. Its internal walls containing a few floor beams and a sprayed souvenir from a graffiti artist. Standing three storeys high it is constructed of red brick, but is rendered from the level at the top of the ground floor doorway to the curb. At the base, the wall thickness measures 2 feet 6 inches, while the internal diameter is 19 feet. There are eight window ways and two ground floor doorways, both at 6 feet 10 inches by 3 feet.

Castor tower mill early this century, showing the remnants of its four clockwise patent sails and 'Lincs' style fan cradle.
[Photo: Peterborough Museum and Art Gallery]

The tower, virtually empty except for a few floor beams in the summer of 1988. [Photo: The author]

One northern window at the second floor has been bricked up and cemented over, but beneath it an ornate wooden sill remains in place. At the top of the brickwork the curb retainer irons hang vertically, two of them extending down to be bolted to the second floor beams, while four others end at the level of the top of the second floor windows. The bottom floor is earth, and generally the ground storey is bare apart from a single iron picket ring in the wall.

In its working days the tower mill bore a rather neat appearance, similar to a miniature Lincolnshire tower with its vertically boarded ogee cap topped with a tall finial and decorative ball. Four patent sweeps, possibly clockwise turning and single shuttered (based on the photograph) made up the sail arrangement, and the fan cradle, styled in the Lincs fashion, seated the fan high above the cap.

Castor wind and watermills are depicted on the Eyre and Jefferys map of 1779, but are absent on Greenwood's edition of 1825/26, although 'Castor Mills' is marked on the Ordnance Survey map of 1824. Another early reference, documented in the *Stamford Mercury* of April 1809, announced the sale of a 'corn smock mill'. This sometimes causes confusion, as many old sale notices fail to give specific details. During the eighteenth and nineteenth centuries it was not uncommon for a tower mill to be recorded as a 'Stone Smock Mill' (see Northampton windpump on page 101), but at other times even the 'Stone' was a descriptive luxury. The advertisement briefed upon the windmill's internal workings, including its two stone pairs, flour machine and 'corn screen'. Interested parties were to contact the owner Mr Joseph Brown. The purchaser may have been a Mr Callow, for in January 1810 a notice appeared in the *Mercury* appealing for persons who may have had any claims to make on the estate of the 'late Mr Callow'. It seems the mills remained within ownership of the family, for in the 1847 trade directory John Thomas Callow is listed as operating the Castor mills, which he continued to do until his death in 1850.

The same year some minor possessions were sold off, including items of furniture and a small number of milling artifacts. Some of the spare parts under offer are obviously linked with the windmill. For instance, two 30 foot sails and an 'Oak Mill Back' [another term for the sail stock], and possibly an iron shaft together with various gears.

By 1864 both mills were acquired by Mr Richard Freeman, who ran them well into the late 1880s. The directory for 1890 indicates that Mr R. A. Loweth had taken over operations, and he is noted for being the last windmiller at Castor. After 1898 he was recorded as working with water power only, which he continued to do well into the 1930s. Unfortunately, the early years of the twentieth century were ones of abandonment for the windmill, the first casualties of neglect being the sails and fan, which were allowed to deteriorate to such an extent that by the time the accompanying photograph was taken only fragments of the sweeps were left. Possibly because of its proximity to the riverside footpath, all potentially dangerous parts were removed, including the cap, sails and all the heavy beams that made up the headframe. By 1933 the windmill was no more than a capless tower.

Arthur C. Smith included the shell in his 1974 survey 'Windmills in Huntingdon and Peterborough', and the same year Peter J. Dolman wrote of the mill's contemporary state in an article about the 'Windmills of Huntingdon' for *Cambridge, Huntingdon and Peterborough Life Magazine*. Although only depicted as a ruin on the 1988 Ordnance Survey map, the mill tower can be seen by those travelling on the preserved Nene Valley railway line between Wansford and Peterborough.

EYE SMOCK MILL

Of the five windmills that originally stood at Eye only two survived into the twentieth century. One of them was the famous tall eight-sailer, the other a less well known but equally interesting smock mill. This was located not far from 'The Greyhound' public house at Eye Green and is noted for being only one of two smock mills that could be found within Northamptonshire after 1900. Unlike its counterpart at Rushden (see page 115), which featured a single storey base and a dome cap, Eye Green mill stood upon shallow brick foundations and was topped with a boat cap. Octagonal in plan, the wooden tower was three storeys high and covered with three layers of weatherboarding, set horizontally, vertically and finally diagonally. The vertically boarded cap may have been winded (in the author's opinion) by a 'Y' wheel and chain, as close examination of photographs fails to reveal any signs of a fan cradle. However, it is possible that a tailpole was used, especially during the early part of the mill's life.

Although it was not marked on the Eyre and Jefferys map of 1779 Eye Green smock mill was alleged to be around 200 years old in 1934. An inscription dating from the eighteenth century was said to have been carved somewhere within its wooden body but sadly no further details were recorded. An early sale notice, which appeared in the *Stamford Mercury* of March 1809, advertised a large smock mill with one pair of French stones, 4 $1/_2$ feet, and one pair of Derbyshire peaks. Also mentioned were two dressing machines, all within the parish of Eye.

The mill was depicted on Bryant's 1824-26 map and was included on the 1824 Ordnance Survey. William Palmer, a local miller and baker, is known to have owned a number of windmills in the Eye district during the early nineteenth century. In March 1838 he placed an announcement in the *Mercury* notifying millers and millwrights of the sale of two surplus common sails measuring 30 feet in length. They had recently been replaced by patent sweeps, but exactly at which mill was unclear. Palmer was listed in the 1847 and 1854 directories, but by 1861 Joseph Collins had taken over.

Another key figure in the district was Mr Benjamin Nix, recorded as baker between 1847 and 1861. A year later he was listed as a miller, while the Royal directory of 1866 documented him as a baker, miller and grocer. By 1870 Mr Nix had ceased milling to concentrate on his bakery business. Meanwhile, Joseph Collins continued grinding up until the turn of the century. (At this point it should be made clear that, unlike other traders, all the aforementioned gentlemen were catalogued as 'Eye millers' and no distinction was made between Eye and Eye Green.)

In 1873 William Oldham, then aged 21, purchased the old smock mill from the Moore family who had held, and leased, the structure for many years. The Oldhams were an old established family of millers originating from Deeping St James in Lincolnshire. William's grandfather is known to have worked the post mill that once stood north of the town where a second windmill, a tower mill, was located. Incredibly, a piece of the post mill's equipment (namely a wooden grain hopper) still exists and has been seen by a friend of the author. Upon its side is carved 'OLDHAM'

Eye smock mill as seen in the late 1930s with large sections of boarding missing from the base of the wooden tower. Note the extensions to the cant posts seemingly propping up the tower. These were, in fact, extensions built on to the originals which are resting on the brick base as normal.
[Photo: Donald Muggeridge]

and possibly the date '1839'.

Although William's father never ventured into corn milling his relations were deeply involved in the business. At one time or another Oldhams ran the tower mills at Werrington, Northamptonshire (see page 184), Wymondham in Leicestershire, and Gainsborough in Lincolnshire. William Oldham continued with the family tradition but it was not without its problems. In a newspaper interview during the 1930s he recalled that work at the smock mill was very hard and the rewards were few.

In 1906 William left the Eye Green mill to take up milling at the eight-sailer (then operating with four sweeps). He was 54 years old. Left unattended and without proper repairs the ancient wooden structure soon fell into a ruinous condition. A drawing from the late 1920s early 1930s (preserved in postcard form) depicts the smock mill lacking sails, but retaining one pair of sail stocks. Another drawing, by Karl S. Wood in June 1933, reveals a great deal of damage to the boarding around the poll-end.

The most detailed record of the derelict mill is by Donald Muggeridge who photographed the ruin in August 1934. By that time the sail stocks had been removed,

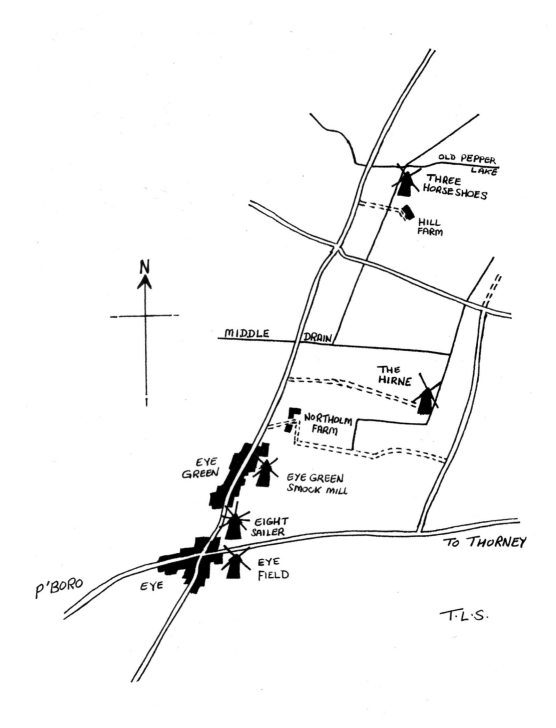

A sketch displaying the relative positions of windmills within the Eye district.

and large sections of weatherboarding at the base of the tower were missing. The photograph shows the wooden tower seemingly standing upon its cant (corner) posts, but on close examination one will notice that these are extensions of the original posts which are behind them resting on the brick base in the normal manner. It is possible that this was a vain attempt to prevent the structure from collapsing, but by 1947 it no longer mattered. That year the Soke of Peterborough's last smock mill was demolished, and the site is now part of a pond.

EYE TOWER MILL

If the theory about Millfield mill is correct (see Peterborough tower mill on page 178) then Northamptonshire would have been one of the few counties in England to possess a five-, six- and eight-sailed windmill, though not all at the same time. Only seven eight-sailers were ever built in the country. The example at Eye was situated not far from the A47 which also passes the tall shell of another eight-sailer at Wisbech.

Like Wisbech Eye mill was graced with an ogee cap fitted with a surrounding gallery and an eight-bladed fantail, although it differed from its cousin by ascending seven floors to the cap instead of Wisbech mill's eight. The two tower mills also boasted a stage, in Eye's case at second floor level. The top of the tower was 'cobbled out' in the Lincolnshire fashion, and the top floor was encircled by two iron bands, but Eye mill's most spectacular features were the eight anti-clockwise, single-shuttered patent sails. Each sail measured 33 feet in length, and differed from the normal arrangement of three shutters to each bay. In most patent sails there were between seven and ten bays, but Eye differed in having four bays of three shutters, and two bays of four, all operated by a web of rods that made up the striking gear. Each sail was individually bolted to an eight-armed iron cross fixed to the 11 inch diameter metal windshaft by means of a number of keys.

Inside, most of the machinery was said to have been of metal construction, including the wallower. It was made up of an eight-piece iron rim bolted to the arms, and the whole assembly, fixed to the upright shaft, claimed to be the largest in the area, with a diameter of 7 inches. At the base of the shaft was the great spur wheel comprising an iron hub in two halves. Eight wooden spokes and an iron rim with wooden teeth completed the assembly, the rim again constructed in eight sections. The four pairs of stones, three French and one peak, were overdriven, and were controlled by a single master governor. Of the stone nuts, two were metal with wooden teeth, while the other two were solid iron castings. The main over-driven machinery and the stones themselves were located on the second floor, while the third and fifth floors were occupied by grain bins.

Eye tower mill was said to have been built in 1836, but this claim is inconsistent with maps dating from 1824 where a mill is depicted on the site. It is known, however, that the tower was heightened to its familiar seven storeys sometime during the 1850s. At that time William Palmer was running the mill, posssibly along with the nearby smock mill at Eye Green (see page 160). By 1861 Mr Joseph Collins had taken charge of the eight-sailer and continued with the business for many years afterwards. Even a violent gale, described as a 'great hurricane' by *The Stamford Mercury* of 29 March 1895, failed to put the mill out of action for long. Some damage was sustained, however. Such was the force of the wind that almost fifty shutters were ripped out of the eight sails.

Three years later, in 1898, Kelly's directory listed Mr Collins as a miller and corn merchant operating with wind and steam power. In October that same year an

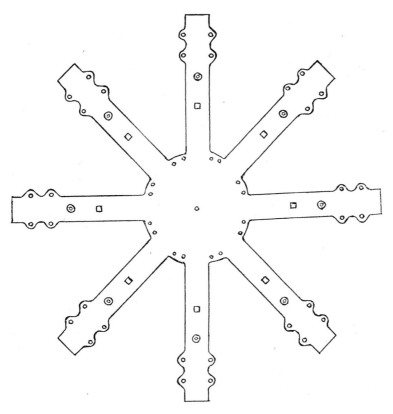

The '8-armed cross' of the Eye mill. [Sketch © by D. Underwood 1989]

advertisement appeared in *The Miller* announcing that the tower mill was for sale as a result of the owner's death. The notice gave details of the various machines installed within the building, and of the two-storey granary linked to the windmill by means of a covered passageway. A similar advert in December described the mill and its equipment in more detail. Amongst the additional machinery was a vertical smutter — a kind of cleaning machine — situated on the fourth floor. It was powered by a vertical shaft (described in Simmons's notes as 'an auxiliary upright shaft') driven from the great spur wheel two floors below. On the ground floor, drive shafts took power to various dressing machines and crushers. The steam engine was recorded as an 8 horse power Gimson and it was contained within an adjacent boiler house.

The next owners were the Keeble brothers, who subsequently sold the windmill for £300 to William Oldham in March 1906. After three decades of grinding at the smock mill William must have felt confident enough to tackle the technologically superior tower mill, but no doubt there were times when the elderly miller would curse the endless flights of steps. During Oldham's first year at the mill, four of the sails were removed, and it was not until around 1908 that it was restored to its full complement of eight. At some time or another the tower mill worked with six sails, then four. There were suggestions that the mill worked better with eight sweeps, but some millers claimed their windmills ran just as well on a lesser number of sails. The multi-sailed mill had advantages of easier starting, even running and greater driving power,

Eye tower mill in all its glory. This was one of only seven 8-sailed windmills ever built in England. [Photo: Peterborough Museum and Art Gallery]

although it was also possible for a mill to be 'overcrowded' with sail, each sweep literally upsetting the airflow to the following one.

When seen and photographed by Donald Muggeridge in August 1934 the mill had reverted to four sweeps. A few months later, in November, *The Peterborough Advertiser* ran a story about William Oldham and his work at the mill. At 82 years old he was believed to be the oldest miller still working in England. The report was aptly titled 'The Octogenarian Miller', and the journalist was quite surprised to find the elderly owner hoisting grain sacks to the bins. In the article William claimed that the popular fine white flour was not so nourishing as the much coarser stoneground variety: a well known fact in these days of high fibre diets. William may have been assisted by his son James who took over after his father's death in 1938. Meanwhile, the mill itself needed constant maintenance. By 1937 the tower had been completely rendered, and a year later a new breast beam was fitted.

Employees at Eye mill included Harry Brown and his brother Frank, who now works at the Peterborough City Museum. One of Frank's tasks was the dressing of the stones or, as he put it, 'chipping the stones'. Other workers included Tom Glover and Mr J. J. Rowell, who recalled in a letter to the Museum the unsocial working

Eye mill in 1934 with only four sails. Note the inclined covered way from the first floor of the tower to the steam mill behind. [Photo: Donald W. Muggeridge]

hours: 'I used to get up in the middle of the night to turn the sails into the wind. Sometimes, when there was a strong wind, I have been grinding corn until 1 or 2 o'clock in the morning.' During one such occasion Mr Rowell witnessed the overwhelming power of the wind. 'We were out one Sunday night when a storm came up and fetched off one of the sails. It fell into the field close to where the police house is now.'

Mr Rowell spent six years at Eye mill, and one of the final jobs he undertook was to assist with the removal of the sails in 1948. The previous year the tower mill had been visited by Rex Wailes who carried out a detailed inspection of the machinery. The results of his examination were passed on to the Society for the Protection of Ancient Buildings and were later published in the *Transactions of the Newcomen Society*. After viewing the interior of the mill Mr Wailes ventured onto the fanstage and made his

Only the tower itself was left by 1968. [Photo: Nigel Moon]

The truncated tower of Eye mill in 1980. Two years later the stump was demolished. [Photo: The author]

way round the gallery to the iron cross where he proceeded to take measurements. His notes complete, Rex was about to return to the fanstage, but could not fail to notice the dangerous condition of the gallery's supports which had rotted to an alarming extent and threatened to give way. Unable to re-enter the mill through the cap's storm hatch — situated just above the windshaft — Mr Wailes was faced with a very precarious return journey, though thankfully without any mishaps. Wailes later described Eye mill as derelict in 1950, the sails were missing, but the fanstage (and presumably the cap) was still in place. In 1952 Mr Joe Odam acquired the mill and incorporated it into his corn and grain supply business.

Inevitably safety demanded that the cap, gallery and fan cradle be removed. The machinery, too, may have been taken out at the same time. By 1968, when it was photographed by Nigel Moon, the tower was still at its full height, but the cobbled out top had been cemented to give a much more rounded appearance, and it was crenellated. Rendering had disguised all traces of the second floor stage, and the white tower contrasted with the two black steel bands strengthening the sixth floor.

In 1971 Mr Odam was forced to truncate the tower as the brickwork of the upper floors had become unsafe. The winters of 1969 and 1970 had taken their toll of the structure, rotting the bricks, despite a lot of money having been spent in maintenance and repairs. A team from the East Anglian Steeplejack Company was hired to carry out the task. The end result was a three-storeyed stump covered by a flat roof. It appeared in Arthur C. Smith's survey *Windmills in Huntingdon and Peterborough* where it was described as 'preserved in good condition'. At that time it is known that the stump was used as a store. Sadly, in 1982 the truncation was totally demolished, and now only two millstones remain at the gateway of the plant, serving as reminders of the last of the Eye mills.

NEW FLETTON TOWER MILL

(although in fact a Huntingdonshire site, this mill has been included because of its close
links with the Soke of Peterborough)

Claimed to have been built in 1870 the large five-storey mill with its crenellated top
was, until demolished in the early 1970s, the last of a long line of windmills at Fletton,
stretching back to the Elizabethan age. It was in 1592 or 1593 that a record of the
manor mentioned a windmill along with various other properties. This was the first of
many references to windmills here. Several sales documents and announcements
recorded mills throughout the sixteenth, seventeenth and eighteenth centuries. In
1769 an enclosure award was drawn up listing a mill in Borough Field, the final site.
Subsequent replacements were to be built at this location between the London Road
(now the A15) and the later railway line.

During the nineteenth century numerous advertisements appeared in *The Stamford
Mercury* relating to Fletton mills. One, of 1822, stated that a smock mill with
bakehouse was to be let. Between 1845 and 1846 Mr J. Adams was working the mill
and advertising for an apprentice miller. Later, in 1847, Mr Adams transferred his
business to Lincoln Road near the Dogsthorpe area of Peterborough.

The most informative advertisment to emerge from the *Mercury* appeared in July
1846. A sale by private contract notice described 'a capital wind tower mill with
patent sails and fantail ...' It went on to mention the stone arrangement of two pairs of
French burrs and a set of grey stones, as well as a mill house and bakery, all being
situated close to the railway. Applications were to be made to the owner Mr James
Empringham. During the 1850s Mr William J. Richardson and Mr J. S. Cassitt were
recorded as millers and bakers, but Mr Empringham was probably responsible for
expanding the business. By the end of the 1850s outbuildings, including the steam
mill, offices, bakery, storage sheds and the mill house, formed a yard around the tower
mill. The initials 'J.E.' and the date '1857' appeared on the newly built adjoining steam
mill. Three years before, steam power had been established at Fletton. An
advertisement of the period noted that the tower mill and a 10 horse power engine
were each powering two pairs of stones. By 1864 the firm of Cadge & Colman Corn
Millers had taken over, and were listed in Kelly's directory of 1869. After that date
they moved to Station Road and were still milling as late as 1936.

At this point one can only speculate at how the date '1870' became relevant to the
tower mill. Perhaps there was major rebuilding after storm damage, or maybe the mill
was raised. (Many of the surrounding outbuildings were two floors in height, and in
the author's opinion give strength to the theory.) Whatever, when completed, the five-
storey tower was covered by an ogee cap and carried patent sails. Mr J. E. Miles was
conducting operations at Fletton in 1871, and the mill is known to have been working
still by 1884 when Swinton and Son were listed as millers. *The Peterborough Trade
Directory* records the business as being situated near 'The Peacock' public house.

Exactly when the windmill ceased work is uncertain, but by March 1921 it had
been sold for £375. Some four years later it was nothing more than an empty tower;
cap, headframe and sails having been removed, and the top of the mill's tower was

crenellated. Most of the machinery and stones were taken out, but the internal flooring was left in place. A flat roof may have existed, but later reports indicated this was not so, meaning the dust floor would have had to bear the brunt of the British weather.

Although not one of the county's more attractive windmill sites, it was not overlooked by enthusiasts. During August 1933 the artist Karl S. Wood depicted the building as a capless tower near the railway line. One year later Donald W. Muggeridge photographed it complete with an advertising hoarding for 'Nestles Milk'. Rex Wailes catalogued the mill (now referred to as New Fletton) in his papers which were later documented in *The Transactions of the Newcomen Society* of 1950, featuring 'The Windmills of Cambridgeshire, including those of the Isle of Ely, Soke of Peterborough and Huntingdonshire' where it was described as a shell in 1925 and 1950.

A thorough inspection of the mill was carried out on 18 February 1973 by local historian Mr C. L. George, who later passed details on to the Peterborough Museum. Mr George discovered that the large mill house had been knocked down two years before, although for the time being the rest of the yard had been spared from redevelopment, but the general feeling was that the mill's future was uncertain. At that time the tower mill had found a new use, the ground floor with its double doors having become a garage, while the first and second floors were taken over by a radio

Fletton tower mill in 1934. [Photo: Donald W. Muggeridge]

club, who evidently were responsible for attaching an aerial to the top of the structure. Within, every available space was crammed with spare parts. Old non-working radio sets, televisions and pieces of furniture were to be seen everywhere, but the upper storeys were inaccessible. Mr George noted that there was no roof. However, upon the eastern wall a cast iron sack hoist remained in good condition and possibly in working order. The offices were derelict, and the rest of the outbuildings had not fared any better, but they had been put to use by a small engineering company.

A small firm of steeplejacks also occupied some property, and along with the engineers, paid rent to a Mr Dobson who owned a nearby shop and at one time had lived in the old mill house.

In August that same year, Arthur C. Smith researched the Soke for his book *Windmills in Huntingdon and Peterborough* in which a photograph and some brief details of the mill can be found. Before he had completed the work Mr Smith was forced to add the sad fact that New Fletton tower mill had been demolished in early 1974.

It seems that a year before the local council were contemplating the possibilities of preservation, but a sale to the Watney's Brewery Company was already in progress. Within a very short time the tower mill was dismantled. The outbuildings followed in April 1974, which coincided with the publication of the *Cambridgeshire, Huntingdon and Peterborough Life* magazine featuring an article by Peter Dolman on the 'Windmills of Huntingdon' describing the remaining structures. Mr Dolman wrote of the New Fletton demolition with regret, as the Soke 'will lose an interesting old landmark.'

PETERBOROUGH POST MILL

According to Baker's map of 1821, and the slightly later Ordnance Survey maps, a total of twelve corn grinding windmills and one windpump stood within the Soke of Peterborough. Of that number three were located in the city centre, these being the tower mill near Dogsthorpe (later Millfield) and two post mills, one at Thorpe Road and the second at Fengate. The latter mill was situated only half a mile east of Peterborough Cathedral, standing on the west side of Car Dyke. Fengate post mill was marked on Greenwood's county map of 1825/26 and could be traced on the earlier Eyre's map of 1779. Regrettably, as in so many cases, the date of erection is not known, but in 1937 it was said to have been at least 200 years old.

Fengate mill could be described as a very rustic post mill with its open trestle structure and four common sails. The buck was horizontally boarded, and from photographs it is evident that the roof was covered in tarred felt on top of board. Typically, as with all Northamptonshire post mills, the only means of bringing the mill into wind was by the use of a tailpole. The whole structure stood upon a mound not far from a very primitive stone-built building that served as the mill house.

Apart from the maps, another early reference was found in the Sun Fire Insurance Company records. During November 1781 a baker, Mr William Dodson, was recorded as having taken out a policy protecting his various properties which included his home, offices and the bakery; all valued at £400. The windmill was insured for £50, as was the mill house — then rented by the miller Thomas Pepper. In 1801 Mr Dodson surrendered an amount of land including the windmill to his son, also William Dodson. Four years later he had sold the property to Mr John Clark of Somersham, who was described as 'a gentleman'. By 1809 the mill had passed to Mr James Holdich who, unlike his predecessor, was content to remain at Fengate for the rest of his life. Together with his wife, Margaret, he set up home in the old mill house, which was rumoured to have been an inn at one time. The low quaint structure with its extremely thick walls and thatched roof was described as a very charming building of great age, but regardless of these features the demand arose for a larger house. When completed the new dwelling was named 'Fengate House' whereas the old stone structure continued to be known as 'The Mill House'.

James Holdich was recorded in Pigot's Commercial Directory of 1830 as a Peterborough miller (his name being mispelt as 'Holditch'). At this time he was also charged with the running of the post mill at Thorpe Road. In appearance it differed little from Fengate but possessed the added luxury of a roundhouse. A report in *The Stamford Mercury* of 31 December 1841 tells of how on the night of the 24th a post mill in the town, together with a number of other buildings, escaped damage or possible destruction by burning, when a group of vagrants entered one of the outbuildings and lit a fire. It was luck that prevented the fire from spreading, as many of the buildings, including the mill's roundhouse roof, were thatched. Although 'Thorpe Road' is not mentioned in the account, it seems probable that this was the mill

In full sail. At the time of its destruction in 1919 Fengate mill was the last surviving post mill within the Soke of Peterborough. [Photo: Peterborough Museum and Art Gallery]

in question. The miller was named as George Morris, but Holdich continued to be linked with the Thorpe Road mill.

In March 1849 he advertised in the *Mercury* for a secondhand windshaft of either wood or metal for his Peterborough mill, and on his 80th birthday his savings and part of his estate, including the mill, were shared out to his family. Unfortunately confusion over the lease led to an amount of land being lost to the Ecclesiastical Commissioners. William Holdich's name cropped up in the 1854 trade directory as miller of Thorpe Road, two years after James Holdich's death in September 1852.

Some time between 1867 and 1870 Thorpe Road post mill was burned to the ground. It was to be the shape of things to come.

Upon the death of James Holdich, Fengate Mill passed to Mr James Newton and after many years, on 21 May 1884, it was auctioned off. A detailed advertisement had listed various properties, including the house, bakery and other outbuildings (including a dovecote). It claimed that the windmill was equipped with 'two pairs of stones, dressing and smut machines' as well as 'going gears and tackle'. It was reported to be in the occupation of Mr Robert Bodger.

The buyer was Frederick White Holdich, grandson of the late James Holdich. Frederick immediately rented the post mill to Mr George Roughton, and over the next 30 years Mr Holdich devoted all his efforts to expanding the farm. As well as stables, a coachhouse and a forging shed, an area was set aside for workshops and a paint store. The machine shop contained a number of lathes, drilling machines and saw benches. Mr Holdich later obtained a chaff cutter and various portable steam engines and road locomotives which were leased out to other farms together with threshing machines and elevators. The business was growing rapidly.

One local attraction was a ballroom set on the first floor of a barn, but pride of place went to the post mill which was regarded more as a family heirloom.

A fine study of Fengate post mill. The 'hut' in the foreground is actually an old railway coach. [Photo: Peterborough Museum and Art Gallery]

THE P.

Fengate Post Mill Destroyed on Friday

[THE FENGATE POST MILL, destroyed by fire on Friday, as it appeared when in full working order. With others at Whittlesey, Yaxley, Crowland, Thorpe, c., it had been in possession of the Holdich family since the 16th Century. Over renty years ago it was taken by Mr. George Allen, of Huntly Grove, Peterborough, ho entirely renovated the inside, but after four years he gave it up, one of the ... *[illegible]* ...

ROUGH ADVERTISER, SATURDAY, MAY 10, 1919.

The OLD POST MILL at FENGATE: All that is Left of It

THE FIRE at Mr. F. W. Holdich's Farm at Fengate, Peterborough, on Friday (as reported in our last issue), was most complete in its destruction. The greatest sight was probably the firing of the venerable Windmill —one of the few post mills now left in the district. It had long since been out of work and out of gear—indeed, it was only suffered to exist because of its extreme antiquity and to its having become a picturesque feature of the district. It was wholly of wood, and its long gaunt sails had for ages shed their shutters and only the beams remained. As soon as the structure was licked by the flames which were driven by the strong wind towards it from the half-acre of furnace adjacent, it was devoured in less than 10 minutes. It was a great crackling holocaust, and the old mill went to its doom swiftly and completely. Indeed, look at all that's left of it! Together with the Thorpe Road Mill and the Millhold Mill, it provided Peterborough with flour for many a generation. As it was in its heyday is preserved to us in the adjacent picture we ... able to give by the courtesy of the family in whose possession it for a long time was ...

These two photographs appeared in The Peterborough Advertiser *on 10 May 1919, a day after the fire. Some exaggerations are noticable, including '16th century' and '... shed their shutters', as the mill clearly ran with common sails. [Photos: Margaret Holdich — reproduced with permission of* The Peterborough Evening Telegraph]

Around 1894 the mill was leased to Mr George Allen of Huntly Grove, Peterborough. He ran a baker's shop and was a friend of John Adams, miller of the multi-sailed tower mill near Dogsthorpe. Mr Allen undertook many major repairs to the post mill, including the renovation of the interior. In 1903 the mill ceased work. One reason often given by the miller was that the flow of wind to the sails was blocked by the cathedral! After leaving the windmill George Allen continued to live locally until his death in 1936.

For many years Fengate Mill remained in a semi-preserved state, the sails having been removed and only the stocks left intact. It was marked on the Ordnance Survey map of 1905 as an 'Old Windmill', perhaps emphasizing its abandonment. Although it seems its value was appreciated, and many were eager to see the mill preserved.

History repeated itself for the Holdich family on the morning of Friday, 9 May 1919, when a fire broke out in a large elevator shed. It was noticed by William Burrow, an engine driver employed by Frederick Holdich. It was 5.30 a.m. when he gave the alarm. The Fire Brigade were alerted half an hour later. When they arrived, haystacks and some outbuildings were already well ablaze. Fanned by a south-westerly gale, the flames threatened to engulf Fengate House. Saving this became the firefighters' main priority, and the sheds were sacrificed. By now the blaze was spreading with frightening speed, and soon the workshops and sheds containing the farm machinery were swallowed up in the inferno. The Holdich family worked feverishly to save their property. Mrs Holdich and her two daughters assisted the firemen, while Frederick was engaged in trying to save his favourite horse from the burning stables. After smashing open the doors and placing a sack over the animal's head he was in the process of leading it out when the roof collapsed, showering him with flaming debris, setting his clothes alight. Although he suffered serious burns to his hands and back he continued to salvage as much as possible. By this time the blaze covered half an acre.

The post mill stood 300 yards from the flaming workshops, but burning debris was carried by the strong wind and soon ignited the veteran. Fengate windmill's destruction took no more than ten minutes. One eye witness said: 'There was just one short, lurid flare and the mill was wiped out.'

Covering the event was *The Peterborough Advertiser* which went to press while the fires were still raging. Only after the last of the flames had been extinguished did Frederick Holdich seek medical assistance. Although his burns were severe it was nothing compared to the heartbreak he is said to have suffered. Years of work had been almost totally destroyed within one day.

Thankfully the family home, 'Old Mill House', and the ballroom were saved, but the workshops with their lathes were lost, as were a number of implements, including a traction engine valued at £600. Also ruined were the stables, a store containing £400 worth of timber, and, most tragic of all, the ancient post mill. Only charred heaps of timber and twisted pieces of metalwork marked their existence. An ex-soldier likened the scene to a Great War battlefield. The total cost of the damage was estimated at £10,000. Mr Holdich claimed that his insurances would only cover £6,000.

In June 1937 a feature on the mill appeared in a local paper. At that time Fengate House remained in the possession of the Holdich family, and the mound upon which the mill had stood was still very prominent. Descendants of the owners can still be found, including Miss Margaret Holdich, who lives at an east coast seaside town. It was Miss Holdich who told the author of the final hammer blow to history which came relatively recently when the ancient mill house was senselessly destroyed to accommodate the ring road around Peterborough.

PETERBOROUGH TOWER MILL

At the turn of the century only two windmills of an original three survived within the boundaries of the City of Peterborough. Fengate post mill stood three-quarters of a mile east of the cathedral, while an attractive tower mill was located a mile north-west of the city centre at Millfield near Dogsthorpe. Overlooking the Lincoln road, the tower mill, which had been constructed in 1831 to replace a post mill, was brick built, four storeys high and finished with a protective coating of tar. Photographs from the 1900s show the structure adorned with an ogee cap, and carrying six single-shuttered, anti-clockwise patent sails winded by a six-vaned fantail. However, many early references indicate that the windmill was originally equipped with five sweeps.

A *Stamford Mercury* advertisment of February 1832 described a newly built 'smock mill' with three pairs of stones, two dressing machines and an unknown number of patent sails, to be let. Any applications would be received by Mr Stephen Pauling. Three years later, in October 1835, the windmill was put up for auction. This time a

'Adams's Mill' at the turn of the century, with six sails. [Photo: Peterborough Museum and Art Gallery]

The mill, some time later when owned by James Garner, who can be seen near the horse-drawn cart. Notable differences include the re-painted cap and the small single storey building attached to the tower. [Photo: Peterborough Museum and Art Gallery]

much more detailed announcement claimed that the five-sailed 'brick built smock mill' was situated on the Lincoln road 'within Dogsthorpe' (it seems Millfield had not yet been formed into a district at this time). The tower mill, together with the mill house and outbuildings were copyhold to Boroughbury Manor. The notice stipulated that if the property was not sold the owners were quite willing to let.

One interested party may have been Mr William Baker who took charge of the windmill, but within a short time ran into problems. By July 1840 Baker had been sent to the debtors prison at Peterborough Jail, itself almost opposite the third of the City's windmills at Thorpe Road. In September representatives for the Manor arranged another sale.

Finally, in 1846/47, a new owner was found in the shape of Mr John Adams, a devout Christian who had previously operated the tower mill at Fletton. Mr Adams was to enjoy many years of milling and baking at Peterborough, and not surprisingly his windmill soon became affectionately known as 'Adams's Mill'. In later life he

'Adams's Mill' in August 1934, three years before its destruction.
[Photo: Donald W. Muggeridge]

befriended George Allen who ran the ancient post mill at Fengate (see page 173). Later still, his daughter married Mr T. L. Barrett, a well-known and respected local trader. Meanwhile, John Adams continued working at the tower mill until the early 1890s.

Past trade directories reveal an important change to the district. Within the pages of the 1854 edition, Adams's mill is listed at Dogsthorpe, Peterborough, but by 1864 the area had been recorded as Millfield, suggesting the creation of the new district. During this time Peterborough tower mill became known under many titles, including 'Dogsthorpe Mill' and 'Adams's Mill'. Following the change, though, it was officially recognized as 'Millfield Mill', and in later years it was simply known as 'the six sailed mill'.

At this point one can only speculate when the windmill was altered from a five-sailer to one with six sails. The last reference I know to a five-sailer is in an advertisement for an apprentice miller which appeared in *The Stamford Mercury* of 29 October 1847. Turn of the century photographs show the windmill bearing six sweeps, and although a sail was snapped off in a gale in 1905 there is little evidence to suggest this was when the change occurred. It is more likely the modification took place during the mid to late nineteenth century. Generally the five-sailed mill was claimed to be more efficient than the normal four-sailers, but the loss of a sweep could result in an upset of the balance between the sails, and the mill being put out of action until the damaged unit was repaired or replaced. Those windmills with an even number of sails would spend less time idle, as the miller would simply remove the opposite sweep and balance would be restored. Champion in such situations was the six-sailer which would be able to continue working with four, two or even three sweeps evenly spaced.

By 1894 John Adams had been succeeded by members of the Kendell family. (According to reports of that year the new miller was a Mr David Kendal, but I am assuming that he was a member of the same family whose name seems to have been frequently misspelt.) Towards the last few years of the nineteenth century the tower and the bakery were being run by Mr Arthur Philip Kendell. His name appeared in Kelly's Trade Directory in 1903 as working with both wind and steam power, described as a 'steam driven roller plant'. No doubt Mr Kendell was present during one particular day in late March or early April 1905 when his mill suffered a minor setback. During heavy winds a sail broke free from the working mill and crashed down between the tower and the bakery. Thankfully nobody was hurt and the damage was slight.

A year later David D. Kendell was conducting the business and was responsible for putting the property up for sale in October/November 1906. The buyer, Mr James Garner, had the honour of being 'Millfield's' last miller. Before the First World War Mr Garner had been proud to describe himself as a miller and corn merchant, but after 1916 he, like so many others, was no doubt forced to grind animal feed (see page 182). Kelly's directory for 1920 documented James Garner and Co. as based at No 220 Lincoln Road, and working with wind and steam. Three years later the site was visited by Rex Wailes who reported that the mill was derelict, although the directory for 1924 reveals Mr Garner was still at work — probably with steam power only. This is possibly the period that the sails were removed, leaving the tower complete with cap. By 1935 Donald Muggeridge noted that only the tower remained, the cap and upper machinery having been removed and presumably a flat roof added.

In 1937 the site was sold to a firm of garage owners for redevelopment, and the tower, which appeared to be in good condition from Mr Muggeridge's photograph, was demolished. Adams Garage, now known as 'Adams of Peterborough' occupies the site. The 'Windmill' public house and 'Windmill Road' remain as memorials to the City of Peterborough's last and only multi-sailed windmill.

WERRINGTON TOWER MILL

A windmill has stood at Werrington since the thirteenth century, and happily that tradition continues, even though the present structure is now no more than a featureless tower standing east of the A15 on the old Glinton road. The yellow brick tower mill remains at its full five storeys and is situated behind the old mill house in a recently built up area. At the present time the building is preserved as a store, but the new owner intends to convert the tower into a dwelling complete with a replacement cap. Already steps have been taken to improve the appearance of the mill. All the tarring has been blasted off, giving the brickwork a very clean finish, but also revealing a section of the base that comprises stone blocks. A bungalow has been built onto the tower, and an adjoining doorway added between them. The two original opposing ground floor doorways are raised, and on entering one cannot fail to notice the two central upright wooden posts that support the first floor.

Although most of the machinery was removed in the mid-1950s the floors remain intact with much windmill bric-a-brac, including two governors with their tentering gear, a dresser feed chute, all the original ladders and, upon the first floor, three bedstones — one French and two peaks. At the third floor level a large unidentified casting can be found. It is centrally positioned with one horizontal bar fixed to the wall. Both ends revealed long levers and at its middle are two wheels, a pulley on the right hand side and, on the same axle, a narrow roller on the left. The whole thing stands on four legs, and cast into the metalwork is 'WADSWORTH BOLTON'. Beyond that, only the temporary tarpaulin roof is noticeable.

Outside, I noticed the tower has been topped with two or three courses of red brick supporting the curb, an iron band clamped in position just beneath. Also at this level a selection of coloured light bulbs encircled the tower, and the owner has attached a TV aerial to the top of the brickwork.

It has been stated that this mill was constructed in 1664, although 1636 and 1686 have also been quoted, for at the base of the tower mill a tablet once existed bearing one of the above dates. Sadly, many years ago, the datestone was cemented over during alterations, so the actual year cannot be confirmed. This, however, is not really applicable to the existing mill, as it was erected after 1835 as a replacement for a smock mill burnt down in that year.

The smock mill appeared on Eyre and Jefferys' map of Northamptonshire in 1779, and in 1792 was insured for the sum of £200 by Mr William Palmer with the Sun Fire Insurance Company. On 22 July 1814 a notice appeared in *The Stamford Mercury* announcing the sale of Werrington's 'Wind Corn Mill'. Applications were to be made to Mr John Freeman. The smock mill failed to appear on Greenwood's county map of 1825/26 but was again mentioned in the pages of the *Mercury* during November 1829 when it was offered for sale by auction by William and John Pask.

A brief description mentioned that the working mill contained two stone sets, one peak and one French, and was said to have been equipped with 'metal gears'. It seems

Werrington tower mill with the mill house in the foreground. [Photo: Peterborough Museum and Art Gallery]

the reserve price was not reached, or the mill was withdrawn from the auction, for William Hilton Pask's name cropped up again later, but this time in rather unfortunate circumstances. During the early evening of Monday, 2 March 1835, a fire broke out within the timber-built mill and quickly engulfed it and its contents. It was Mr Pask's good fortune to be insured, and he was able to set about the construction of a replacement windmill — this time a tower mill which was not just built on the same site but on the base or foundations of the former mill.

When completed the tower mill was tarred and would have made an impressive sight with its four anti-clockwise, single-shuttered, patent sails, vertically-boarded ogee cap (finished with a finial but no petticoat) and its eight-bladed fantail. The base diameter measured 20 feet internally and the wall thickness was 1 foot 10 inches. There were three pairs of overdriven stones, the two sets of peaks measuring 4 feet 6 inches and 4 feet 4 inches, while the French burrs were 4 feet 2 inches in diameter. Other equipment included two dressing machines and a 'bolting mill'.

Mr Pask worked the mill through 1847 (he was listed in that year's trade directory) until his death in 1852. Werrington mill was immediately put up for sale. The buyer may have been Mr H. Nix who was recorded in the 1854 directory, but some ten years later it was in the occupation of Mr G. Taylor. For a while during the nineteenth

A good view of Werrington mill after a storm had ripped off two of its sails in 1912. John Tyler is standing on the right holding part of the wreckage.
[Photo: Peterborough Museum and Art Gallery]

century the windmill was copyhold to Werrington Manor. However, by the late 1860s it was in the possession of the Oldham family who enjoyed many decades of prosperity. It was about this time that references to a bakery were made, and in later years a steam engine was introduced to work a fourth pair of stones. Directories listed Mr Marston Oldham as miller and baker at Werrington between 1869 and 1890, whereafter Jason Oldham continued to work using wind and steam power until 1908. It is possible that the Werrington Oldhams may have been connected with the Eye Oldham's (see page 160) who ran the seventeenth century smock mill there at the same time.

In 1908 the tower mill was purchased by Mr Ernest Herbert Goff for £650 (although this conflicts with an entry in Herbert E. S. Simmons's *Notes on Northamptonshire Windmills* which records *The Miller* of 3 August 1908 having claimed that

The last miller at Werrington mill, Ernest Herbert Goff, who ran the mill until he retired in 1953.
[Photo: Peterborough Museum and Art Gallery]

Werrington tower mill had been sold by auction for £500 to Mr Thomas Sculthorpe in July.) Mr Goff continued with the business, and in 1912 employed Mr John Tyler, the stepson of one of the previous millers. Mr Tyler generally assisted Mr Goff in his duties around the mill, which sometimes meant getting up during windy nights to work it.

On one particular night in 1912 a violent storm blew two of the sails off with what was described as 'a most terrible noise'. One sweep smashed through a nearby stone wall, and such was the impact that both sails were totally destroyed. The accident did not stop Mr Goff from milling, and for many years afterwards the windmill continued to turn with the remaining two sails.

In an interview recorded in the Peterborough edition of *The Evening Telegraph* on 17 August 1972, Mr Tyler remembered that the business was capable of producing 300 loaves of bread every day, each one selling for 'tuppence farthing'. He went on to describe the tower mill as 'a big mill by contemporary standards' and very elegant and modern. Mr Tyler had left the mill in 1925 to get married, but remained in the area long after retiring.

During the First World War many wind and watermills suffered heavy casualties owing to government legislation condemning stoneground flour as unfit for human consumpton. As a result many millers took to grinding for animal feed instead.

Werrington mill in August 1934. Though minus fan and sails, the mill continued to work by steam power until 1953. [Photo: Donald W. Muggeridge]

Undaunted, Mr Goff continued to work, but by 1920 it was by steam power only, as the two remaining sails were removed for safety reasons. Directories for the period list Mr Goff as a baker only.

Rex Wailes recorded Werrington tower mill as a derelict in 1923, and a decade later Karl S. Wood and Donald W. Muggeridge depicted the mill in sketch and photograph as a tower at full height with the cap, fan cradle and windshaft all in place. By 1948 these had been removed leaving the tower with a flat roof but still in working condition.

It was not until 1953 that, owing to age and the heavy labour, Ernest Goff was forced to give up work. The mill and bakery, complete with ovens, were sold to Mr and Mrs Hitchcock who had recently moved into the old mill house. Meanwhile, Mr Goff lived out the last few years of his life in retirement until his death in around 1956.

For a short while the Hitchcock family made an attempt to keep the mill grinding oats for pig meal, but it proved to be uneconomical, and inevitably Werrington mill ceased work. Another use had been found for the tower and most of the machinery was taken out leaving the building to become a store. The Hitchcock's son, Keith, later built up a successful organ business, and most of his supplies were housed in the lower floors of the windmill. Even the old oven had a part to play, and became the main showroom.

When seen by Arthur C. Smith in September 1972, during the survey for his book

Werrington tower in 1988. Stripped of its tarring, some of the smock mill foundations were then visible. Some remnants, including three bed stones, were found within. [Photo: The author]

Windmills in Huntingdon and Peterborough, the tower was complete with tarring and windows, ensuring some protection against the weather.

Three years later in April 1975 the Peterborough Museum received a letter from the grandson of Ernest Goff, Mr F. Bird of Glinton, giving details of Werrington's windmills, and claiming records could be traced back to 1215. He also mentioned the inscription upon the date stone as being 1636 or 1686. Another interesting piece of information held by the museum is an undated newspaper cutting from a local edition explaining the arrival of an airmail letter at the Broadwoodwidger Urban Council offices, Devon. The sender was a Mr Wayne Harbour of Iowa, U.S.A., who (with the help of the post office) was trying to trace a village named Werrington which contained a windmill. In the letter Mr Harbour had written that the mill had been leased in 1664 for 1,094 years and must be preserved until 2758. The paper referred to an early Werrington mill of 1291, '667 years ago' (which dates the press cutting in 1958). The American had also enclosed a drawing of the mill.

If any windmill survives until 2758 it will indeed be a miracle. Perhaps Werrington's best chance of accomplishing this is as a house conversion.

PART III

Other Northamptonshire windmills

ASTWELL WINDMILL

This mill (type unknown) was illustrated on various old maps standing a mile south-west of Wappenham near the Helmdon Road. During part of the nineteenth century it was held by the Summers family, and had passed to Mr E. King by 1903. Edwin King and son were recorded using wind power in 1920, but ten years later only steam and water use was listed.

BRIGSTOCK TOWER MILL

Although not appearing on the 1779 map, two windmills are shown east of the village upon Bryant's 1824/26 map with 'Harpers Brook' flowing between them. One windmill stood on the southern side of the Stanion road, while the second mill was located just north of the parallel road to Geddington Chase. Only the Stanion Road mill was depicted on the 1824 Ordnance Survey, this being corroborated by Greenwoods 1825/26 map. The survivor was a five storey tower mill with four sails, a boat cap and a fantail, claimed to have been built in 1635 (unlikely in the author's opinion). Derelict by the turn of the century, without sails or fan, it was sold in 1905 for £12 and subsequently demolished.

The derelict Brigstock tower, with sails and fan removed. The original caption to this photograph claimed the mill was built in 1635. Photo: Cyril E. Diamond]

CRANSLEY WINDMILL

Within the pages of his very detailed study *A Checklist of Northamptonshire Wind and Watermills* Geoffrey H. Starmer includes a reference to a windmill at Cransley near Kettering. It is claimed the mill stood due west of woodland, and was believed to have existed during the late 1930s. No entry was made in the Simmons collection of Northamptonshire windmill records, and in 1980 the author visited the village in an effort to learn more. Elderly locals could only remember a watermill and a wind engine within the parish, and old maps have failed to shed any further light on the subject.

COGENHOE WINDMILL

In August 1942 a lone Dornier 217 bomber attacked Wellingborough. The aircraft had been spotted by members of the Observer Corps said to have been based at Cogenhoe windmill. One of the survivors of that group claims the 'mill' was no more than a two storey stump which was eventually demolished during the 1950s. None of the author's maps or reference books pointed to a windmill ever having been at Cogenhoe, but the Corps member insisted that there was no mistake. In conversation with historian Michael L. Gibson, author of *Aviation in Northamptonshire* (Northamptonshire Libraries) it was learned that the Cogenhoe O.C. section was H3, part of 12 Group based at grid reference SP822606. So far the writer has been unable to determine positively whether a windmill existed at this site.

GLINTON TOWER MILL
(Soke of Peterborough)

Depicted on the 1824 Ordnance Survey map, the mill stood south of the Helpston road (B1443) west of Glinton. For many years it was run by Mr John Webster until around 1877 when William Pridmore was recorded as the miller. The latter continued to work the windmill until it was sold, along with three acres, to Mr W. Howell for £360 in 1909. It had gone by 1934, but some of the outbuildings were said to have survived as late as 1975.

HARGRAVE POST MILL

On pages 156 and 157 of his book *In Search of English Windmills* Stanley Freese referred to a post mill at Hargrave. He wrote that the mill was 'scarcely a hundred yards from the village in Bedfordshire, whilst the village itself is in Northamptonshire.' Unknown to Mr Freese at that time, the derelict post mill actually stood within the boundary of Lower Dean in Bedfordshire. This interesting and unusual veteran survived until 1959 before collapsing.

MOULTON TOWER MILL

A stone-built tower mill four storeys high with a dome cap, four sails, two of them common and two shuttered, winded by an eight-bladed fantail. It was depicted on the 1779 county map, and later damaged by fire in 1843. The tower mill worked in conjunction with a nearby watermill run by Mr J. Aychurch about 1847, and later by Mr T. Merry, whose wife Harriet continued the business, presumably after her husband's death during the late 1850s or early 1860s. At a later date the mills were owned by a Mr Griggs, and eventually passed to the Mulvainey family. The windmill was truncated to two storeys in 1910 after having lost its sails some thirty years before.

In 1954 the tower was little more than a ring of stone foundations two or three feet high. Mr Bill Richardson, who demolished the stump, re-used many of the stones to

Moulton mill depicted with sails by Frank C. Gill. [Reproduced with the permission of R.C. Gill]

rebuild an adjacent wall. The mill's remains are now overgrown and contrast sharply with the watermill which is now a house conversion.

OLD POST MILL

This was an open trestle post mill with four clockwise common sails and tailpole. Located half a mile north of the village of Old, which in past years was known as 'Wold', it outlived a second windmill which stood just east of the village. Both mills were shown on the Eyre and Jefferys map of 1779, but only the northern one featured on subsequent maps. Millers included John Achurch and William Francis. During the 1870s the post mill was run by William Bushby who was recorded in 1885 as working with steam power. It was drawn by Frank C. Gill in 1909 when still in a good state of repair, but said to have been struck by lightning and burnt down around 1910.

STAVERTON POST MILL

A real oddity which has been included in this section as a suitable explanation has yet to be found. This post mill was featured on various old maps standing just south of the road to Leamington Spa (now A425). In 1928 it was described by F. C. Gill as 'long gone', but in his records relating to Northamptonshire windmill sites H. E. S.

*The stump of Moulton mill in 1947.
[Photo: Donald W. Muggeridge]*

*Only the foundations of Moulton mill
remained in 1980, hidden under
overgrowth. [Photo: The author]*

Simmons wrote of a ruined one-time conversion of a two-storeyed post mill roundhouse seen and photographed in 1944. The structure was said to be situated upon 'a tree-capped hill' three quarters of a mile from Daventry. The roof, steps and floors were missing, but 'Syd' calculated the remains as being 16 feet high and having an internal diameter of 18 feet. The photograph (not yet seen by the author) is supposed to exist in the Science Museum Library, where the Simmons collection is currently housed. The site, believed to be 'Big Hill' near Staverton, was explored in 1980 but nothing was found.

SYRESHAM POST MILL

Originally to be seen standing a quarter of a mile north of the village, this mill was reported to have worked with two pairs of stones. The miller in about 1860 was a Mr Joseph Timms, and he was succeeded by Mr Alfred Gee in the early 1890s. The final entry in the trade directories for Syresham mill was in 1906. According to Stanley Freese the mill was felled (or lost) between 1910 and 1920.

The open trestle post mill at Old in 1909 by Frank C. Gill. [Reproduced with the permission of R.C. Gill]

WESTON-ON-THE-WELLAND POST MILL

Known as 'Weston Mill' and 'Sutton Bassett Mill' even though it stood within the parish of Weston-on-the-Welland. It was equipped with a single storey roundhouse, tailpole and two, possibly four, common sails. The miller was Mr William Tilly whose name appears in the 1869 and 1877 directories. Before the turn of the century the sails were shortened to prevent it from injuring the baker's horses which grazed in the mill field. It was pulled down in 1906. However, the mill house still exists as do a number of millstones paved into the ground within Weston.

PART IV

Some vanished windmills predating 1900

ASHLEY (SP795905)   Post mill listed in directories as late as 1894 when Thomas Stafford was the miller.

BRACKLEY (SP595372)   Open trestle post mill with four common sails and tailpole, stood not far from watermill. Said to have been demolished in 1891 to make way for the Great Central Railway.

BARNACK (TF067029)   'Southorpe Mill' in Soke of Peterborough. Stone-built tower mill run by the Morris family until sold in 1835.

BLISWORTH (SP733537)   Post mill with two common and two spring sails, brake and tail wheels. Worked with steam mill until the latter burnt down in 1879. The post mill was put up for sale the same year.

BURTON LATIMER (SP909760)   One of two windmills that stood here during the nineteenth century. Owned by Mr J. Eadey and described in 1884 as being of 'wood and brick' construction. Only steam mill was being used by 1898.

BRIXWORTH (SP757713)   Stood east of village on the Scaldwell road. Millers may have included J. Knight and Job Eagles in 1866. Farm buildings now occupy site.

BULWICK (SP968937)   Depicted on 1824 Ordnance Survey map as 'Bulwick Mill'. Was a post mill with one pair of peaks and a set of burrs. Owned in 1830 by Thomas Preston. The miller in 1854 was W. Shelton.

CRICK (SP592720 and SP590716)   Two windmills are known to have existed here during the nineteenth century around 1869. The northern mill at the first reference and the southern site at the second.

DAVENTRY (SP584620)   'Burrow Hill', also known as 'Borough Hill', (see Newnham on page 93). Directories for 1869 list Mrs A. Wall as miller.

EAST FARNDON (SP712855)   Believed to have been a post mill. Shown on 1779 map. Millers included Charles Smith and George Haynes. The latter was listed as late as 1894.

EYE (TF230028)   Soke of Peterborough post mill located a short distance south of the Thorney road in an area known as 'Eye Field' or 'Blackman's Field'. On 1779 map and 1824 Ordnance Survey. It was sold and possibly dismantled in 1838.

EYE (TF242048)   Soke of Peterborough. Appeared on 1779 map and the 1824 Ordnance Survey map as 'The Hirne'. Bryant's 1824-26 map identified it as a drainage mill. Gone by 1892.

EYE (TF238067)   Soke of Peterborough. 'Three Horseshoes'. The mill is shown on the 1824 Ordnance Survey map and Bryant's map close to a dyke, but there is no suggestion that it was a drainage mill. Not on 1892 Ordnance Survey map.

Great Oakley post mill shortly before its destruction in 1895. [Photo: F.A. Moore]

GREAT OAKLEY (SP869851)   Post mill with an open trestle and four common sails winded by a curved tailpole. The land on which it stood now forms part of the parish of Newton. Mill dismantled in 1895.

HARRINGTON (SP768793)   'Mill Hill' still marked on modern Ordnance Survey maps. The site is not far from a water tower.

HOLLOWELL (SP686717)   Also 'Holywell'. Featured on Jefferys' map and was recorded in the 1885 directory. Curiously, not in Herbert Simmons's collection of Northamptonshire windmill records.

KETTERING (SP866793)   Tower mill known as 'Rockingham Road Mill'. See Kettering post mill (page 77).

KINGS CLIFFE (TL011969)   Smock mill situated south of the Apethorpe road. It contained one pair of peak stones and one pair of French stones. Shown on the 1779 map, and at that time owned by Thomas Boughton. Later owner was George Howles. The cap and sails were blown off in February 1860, and the mill was dismantled shortly afterwards. Crop mark remains.

LAXTON (location unknown)   Not on 1779, 1824, 1825/26 or Ordnance Survey maps. According to Simmons it was an open trestle post mill with anti-clockwise sweeps, two common, two shuttered. An illustration is said to have appeared in *The Dunlop Book of Roadside Sketches*. No date or other details available.

LONG BUCKBY (SP645690)   Post mill. Known as 'Cotton End Mill' and sometimes as 'Gale House Mill', it stood on the West Haddon road. Featured on Bryant's map, it was misplaced on the Greenwood chart.

MAIDFORD (SP615522)   Depicted on Bryant's map and the 1834 Ordnance Survey map. Stood near Blakesley Heath one mile south-east of second Maidford windmill.

MIDDLETON CHENEY (SP489424)   Mr C. Pinfold was the miller in 1874.

MILTON MALSOR (SP742554)   Post mill run by the Bray family until it was demolished in the 1860s.

MORETON PINKNEY (SP582487)   'Moreton Mill' was being run by Mr J. Gardner in 1854. A picture of this mill is held in the Central Library, Northampton, as part of the Dryden Collection. Elderly locals remember that the mill site was known as 'The Windmill Fields' long after its destruction.

NORTHAMPTON (SP764614)   Tower mill stood north-east of the town on the Kettering road (now the A43). Pulled down during the 1880s.

NORTHAMPTON (SP740641)   The 'Windmill' public house, on the Welford road north-west of Kingsthorpe, stands opposite the site of a windmill depicted on the 1779 map. By 1824 the pub, then known as 'Windmill House', had replaced it. Two peak stones survive in the floor of the porchway, and it is claimed that some of the mill's timbers were incorporated in the pub's construction. The painting on its signboard is of a tower mill which seems to have been based on Perrin's picture of Tansor mill (see page 131).

PETERBOROUGH (TL183986)   Post mill known as 'Thorpe Road Mill'. See Peterborough post mill — Fengate (page 173).

PIPEWELL   The earliest record of a Northamptonshire windmill appeared in a document from Pipewell Abbey criticizing local people who between 1143 and 1323 decimated the woodland surrounding the Abbey. It was said that due to the taking of timber to build houses, granaries, watermills and windmills (and the renewing of 'sailyards') the forest was entirely destroyed. The Abbey was abandoned by the monks shortly afterwards.

Rothwell post mill (Cheney's mill) with its four clockwise common sails and tall roundhouse. [Photo: F.A. Moore]

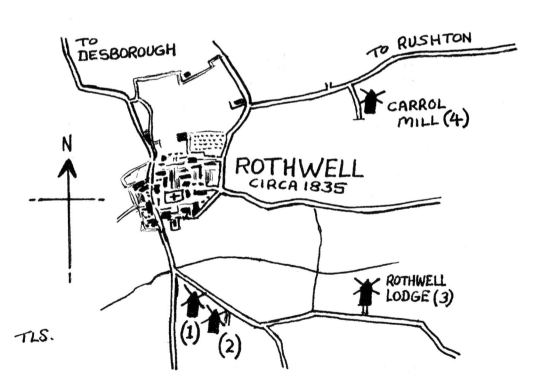

Site
Windmill at Walgrave - drawn on site from description given by a native.

Walgrave's open trestle post mill by Frank C. Gill. The picture was based on a local man's description of the long lost mill. [Reproduced with the permission of R.C. Gill]

ROTHERSTHORPE (SP705564) Smock mill. Depicted on Bryant's map half a mile south-west of village, near crossroads. Titled 'Smock mill' (perhaps emphasizing the rarity of smock mills within the county even then). Captioned 'Thorpe mill' on the 1834 O.S. Run by Sam and Henry Dunkley in 1874.

ROTHWELL (SP820803) Featured on 1779 map half a mile south-east of the village on the Kettering road. Seen in company with second windmill near Rothwell Lodge (see below). First mill was operated by Benjamin Cheney, and possibly was a post mill with four clockwise common sails, tailpole and very tall roundhouse. Site near a cemetery.

ROTHWELL (SP821801) Illustrated on Bryant's map, but not on Greenwood's of the same period. Stood close to Cheney's mill (see page 199) and was owned by the Marriott family. Known as 'Marriott's Mill'.

ROTHWELL (SP836803) Absent on maps preceeding the 1835 Ordnance Survey. Shown just south of Kettering road (now A6) near Rothwell Grange, one and a half miles south-east of Rothwell. This is possibly the mill owned by Mr H. Wright during the 1850s.

ROTHWELL (SP828817) Known as 'Carrol Mill' on the 1835 Ordnance Survey map. Situated south of the Rushton road. It was marked on the 1779 map and is believed to have been worked by the Cheneys.

RUSHDEN (SP951668)   Possibly a smock mill. Known as 'Glassbrook Road Mill'. It is now the site of the 'Windmill Club', although the painting upon its signboard is that of a post mill. May have also been known as 'Green's Mill' after the miller Joseph Green.

STOKE BRUERNE (SP743506)   A tower mill known as 'Stoke Mill'. On the 1834 Survey map standing very close to (now disused) railway embankment.

THRAPSTON (TL001783)   On 1779, 1824 and 1825/26 maps standing south of the town near the Denford road. The miller in 1830 was Mr J. Compton. Not on 1835 map. Thrapston also had two watermills, the northern one of which was tragically demolished in 1986.

WALGRAVE (SP796719)   Open trestle post mill located west of the village not far from a watermill. Both marked on early maps as 'Walgrave Mills'. Drawn by Frank C. Gill from descriptions by local people.

WELLINGBOROUGH (SP909677)   Shown on 1779 map in company with a second windmill and a watermill. By 1824 only one windmill survived together with the watermill, according to Bryant's map, known as 'East Mills'. Lovel Warren was the miller in 1830. Site near the Irthlingborough road, close to the railway line.

WELLINGBOROUGH (SP883692)   'Red Well Mill'. Recorded as 'Rod Well Mill' on Bryant's map. Stood near a watermill known as 'Dicken's Mill'. Site now a housing estate.

Yelvertoft post mill in 1896 as seen by Frank C. Gill. [Reproduced with the permission of R.C. Gill]

WELLINGBOROUGH (SP902698)   'Great Harrowden Mill'.   North of the town near the railway. The site, which appears on the 1824-26 map, now forms part of an industrial estate.

WEST HADDON (SP628725)   Also known as 'Winwick Windmill'. In 1871 Thomas Leeson was listed as miller at Winwick watermill.

WHILTON (SP628645)   Shown on the 1779 map, and much more interestingly recorded on Bryant's map as a 'Mill in ruins'. Mentioned in an advertisement of 1756 claiming the windmill along with other property would be 'held for the residue of a mortgage term of 1,000 years commencing September 1718'. Not on the 1835 Ordnance Survey map.

YELVERTOFT (SP590754)   A post mill run by William Bray along with a steam mill. Located half a mile west of the village, within a small circular enclosure. Towards the end of its life the windmill worked with only two sails. Demolished in 1899.

Glossary

Anchor irons	Vertical iron struts which hold the curb in place.
Batter	Taper of tower.
Bed stone	The lower and static stone of a pair of millstones.
Bolting machine	Another term for a bolter.
Brake	A wooden (or iron) brake shoe which encircles the brake wheel and is operated by a brake lever.
Brake wheel	Drive wheel mounted on windshaft which engages the wallower and can be halted by a surrounding brake shoe.
Bridge tree	A pivoting beam which carries the stone spindle.
Bolter	Early type of flour dresser consisting of an inclined cylindrical frame covered with cloth.
Buck	Body of the post mill.
Cannister	Cast iron fitting located at the end of the windshaft through which the sail stocks passed. Also known as the poll end.
Cap	Rotating cupola mounted on top of smock or tower mill.
Cant posts	Inclined corner posts of a smock mill.
Centering wheels	Horizontally set wheels attached to the cap frame.
Common sails	Cloth-covered sails.
Crenellations (or castellations)	Battlements on top of a converted tower.
Crosstrees	Horizontal cross beams set on piers carrying the quarter bars of a post mill.
Crown tree	The main horizontal beam in a post mill buck which pivots upon the post.
Curb	Wooden or iron track upon which the cap rotates.
Damsel	Spindle on an underdrift stone assembly that causes the grain shoe to vibrate, thus providing feed to the stones.
Derbyshire peaks	Millstones originating from the Derbyshire peak district.
Dressing machine	Machine (bolter, wire machine, etc.) used for separating flour from bran and foreign matter.
Dust floor	Top floor of a tower/smock mill.
Fan cradle	Structure supporting the fantail.
Fanstage	Platform allowing access to the fantails.
Fantail	Fan set at rear of cap for automatically bringing the sails around to face the wind via a series of gears.

French burrs	Millstones constructed in segments, held together with plaster-of-paris and iron bands.
Gallery	A stage situated around the cap of a smock or tower mill.
Governor	A device which prevents the runner stone from rising and increasing the gap between it and the bedstone should the revolutions increase.
Grain cleaner	A belt-driven cylindrical filtering machine.
Great spur wheel	A large drive wheel fitted to the upright shaft engaging the stone nuts.
Grey stones	Peak stones, or Derbyshire Peak millstones
Head frame	Horizontal timbers which form the base frame of the cap (more commonly known as the cap frame).
Hopper	A container supplying grain to the stones.
Horse	A wooden frame situated upon the vat supporting the hopper.
Hurst frame	A raised framework supporting the millstones.
Iron cross	An alternative to the poll-end, allowing 4, 5, 6 or 8 sails to be fitted.
Luffing	Turning the movable part of a mill (i.e. buck of post mill, cap of smock or tower mill) so the sails face the wind.
Luffing gear	A manually operated winding system involving the use of a winch, 'Y' wheel and an endless chain.
Main post	The main upright timber supporting a post mill's body.
Molinologist	One who studies windmills/watermills.
Ogee cap	A wooden-ribbed, onion-shaped cap.
Overdrift (also Overdriven)	Millstones powered from above.
Patent sail	Self-regulating shuttered sails operated by a striking gear passing through the hollow windshaft.
Petticoat	Protective vertical weatherboarding at the base of the cap.
Poll-end	See Cannister.
Post mill	Windmill with its body pivoting upon a main post.
Quant	A vertical overdriven shaft connecting the stone nut to the runner shoe.
Quarterbars	Inclined timbers supporting the main post of a post mill from the crosstrees.
Rack	A toothed ring encircling the top of the tower engaging the winding gear.
Roundhouse	A small building which protects the trestle of a post mill.
Runner stone	Revolving upper millstone of a pair.
Sack hoist	An assembly for lifting sacks to the upper floors.
Sail frames	Framework of sail attached to the whip.

Shoe	A trough from the hopper feeding grain to the millstones.
Shuttered sails	Meaning either spring or patent sails.
Skirt	Additional boarding at the base of a post mill.
Smock mill	A 'capped' windmill with a wooden tower.
Smutter	A small vertical wire machine used for removing smut from wheat.
Spring sails	Shuttered sails worked by a spring-loaded lever on each sweep.
Stage	A platform encircling the tower of a windmill.
Stocks	Timbers that are inserted through the cannister to which the whips are bolted.
Stone dressing	Re-sharpening the cutting face of the millstones.
Stone nuts	Gears driven from the great spur wheel which take power to the stones.
Stone spindle	The iron shaft upon which the runner stone is mounted.
Striking gear	Chain-operated mechanism used for opening and closing the shutters of a patent sail.
Sweeps	An East Anglian term for sails.
Tail pole	Lever used for winding a post mill.
Tail wheel	A drive wheel mounted on the rear of the windshaft powering a second set of stones — a system found in some post mills.
Tail winding	A term used to describe the wind catching the sails from behind, thus causing damage to the mill or its machinery.
Tower mill	A 'capped' windmill with a brick or stone-built tower.
Trestle	The substructure of a post mill consisting of the main post, crosstrees and quarterbars.
Underdrift (also Underdriven)	Millstones powered from below.
Upright shaft	The main vertical drive shaft to which the wallower and the great spur wheel are attached.
Vats (also tuns)	Wooden casing over the millstones.
Wallower	A pinion mounted on top of the upright shaft that engages the brake wheel.
Weather	The pitch or twist of windmill sails.
Whip	The timber that is bolted to the sail stock upon which the sail frame is attached.
Winding	Bringing the sails around to face the correct wind direction (see Luffing).
Windshaft	The inclined sail axle, also carrying the brake wheel.
Wire machine	An improved bolter, able to grade produce with the aid of rotating brushes.
'Y'-wheel	A wheel with 'Y'-shaped forks able to carry an endless chain.

Bibliography

Bailey, John, L.H., *Finedon, otherwise Thingdon* (John L.H. Bailey, 1975).

Bennett, Richard and Elton, John, *History of Corn Milling Vol. 2 'Watermills and Windmills'* (Simpkin, Marshall and Co. Ltd., 1899) (reprinted by E.P. Publishing, 1973).

Cambridgeshire, Huntingdon and Peterborough Life Magazine, various issues.

Freese, Stanley, *Windmills and Millwrighting* (Cambridge University Press, 1957).

Hiller, Richard, *Old Peterborough in Photographs* (Cambridgeshire Libraries and City of Peterborough Museum and Art Gallery, 1979).

Hopkins, R. Thurston, and Freese, Stanley, *In Search of English Windmills* (Cecil Palmer, 1931).

Long, George, *The Mills of Man* (London, 1931).

Mais, S.P.B., *England of the Windmills* (J.M. Dent, 1931).

Markham, Major C.A., *Northamptonshire Notes and Queries* (Taylor and Son).

Moon, Nigel, *The Windmills of Leicestershire and Rutland* (Sycamore Press Ltd, 1981).

Moore, F.A., *Lost and Hidden Kettering* (Kettering Civic Society Publications).

The Newcomen Society Transactions, various volumes.

Northampton County Magazine, 1928-33.

Northamptonshire and Bedfordshire Life magazine, various issues.

Northamptonshire Independent magazine, various issues.

Shillingford, A.E.P., *England's Vanishing Windmills* (Godfrey Cave Associates, 1979).

Simmons, H.E.S., *The Simmons' Collection of Records Relating to British Windmills and Watermills: 'Windmills of Northamptonshire'* (extracts reproduced by courtesy of the Science Museum, London).

Smith, Arthur, C., *Windmills in Huntingdon and Peterborough* (Stevenage Museum Publications, 1977).

Smith, H. Clifford, *Sulgrave and the Washingtons* (Jonathan Cape, 1933).

Starmer, Geoffrey H., *A Checklist of Northamptonshire Wind and Watermills* (1970).

Thompson, Beeby, *Corn Mills, A Study in Evolution* (Journal of the Northamptonshire Natural History Society, 1931).

Vince, J.N.T., *Discovering Windmills* (Shire Publications, 1969).

Wailes, Rex, *Windmills in England* (Architectural Press, 1948).

—   *The English Windmill* (Routledge and Keegan Ltd, 1954).

—   *A Source Book of Windmills* (Ward Lock Ltd, 1979).

Trade Directories

Pigot's 1830, 1840, 1841.

Kelly's 1847, 1854, 1869, 1877, 1885, 1890, 1894, 1898, 1903, 1910, 1920, 1940.
Melvill's 1861.
Slater's 1862.
Royal 1866.
Mercer & Crocker 1870.
Wright's 1884.
Post Office 1869.
Whellan 1874.
Harrods 1876.

Maps

Eyre and Jefferys' 1779 (revised 1791).
A. Bryant 1824-26.
Greenwood and Co. 1825/26.
First Edition *Ordnance Survey* including 1824, 1834, 1835, and various modern
    editions.
Letts, Son and Co. 1864/65.
Carey's New Map 1800

Appendix 1

WINDMILLS IN NORTHAMPTONSHIRE 1900

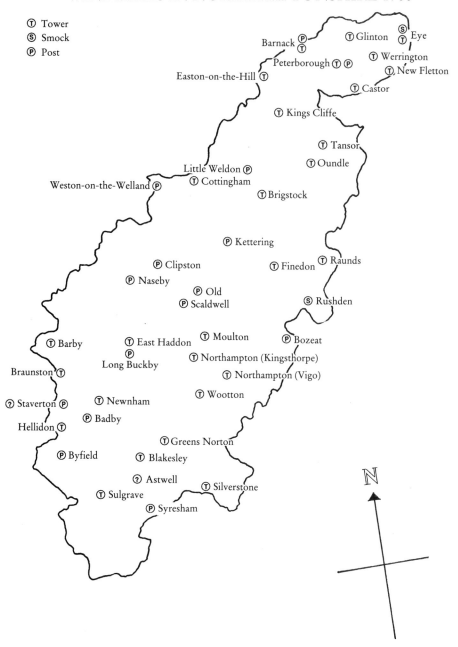

- ⓣ Tower
- ⓢ Smock
- ⓟ Post

Appendix 2

WINDMILLS IN NORTHAMPTONSHIRE 1940

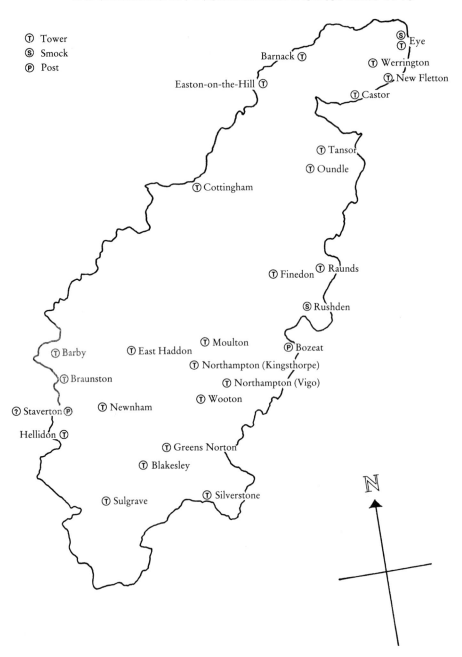

Ⓣ Tower
Ⓢ Smock
Ⓟ Post

Ⓢ Ⓣ Eye
Barnack Ⓣ
Ⓣ Werrington
Ⓣ New Fletton
Easton-on-the-Hill Ⓣ
Ⓣ Castor

Ⓣ Tansor
Ⓣ Oundle

Ⓣ Cottingham

Ⓣ Finedon Ⓣ Raunds

Ⓢ Rushden

Ⓣ Moulton
Ⓣ Barby Ⓣ East Haddon Ⓟ Bozeat
Ⓣ Northampton (Kingsthorpe)
Ⓣ Braunston Ⓣ Northampton (Vigo)
Ⓣ Wooton
Ⓟ Staverton Ⓟ Ⓣ Newnham
Hellidon Ⓣ
Ⓣ Greens Norton
Ⓣ Blakesley
Ⓣ Sulgrave Ⓣ Silverstone

N

Appendix 3

WINDMILLS IN NORTHAMPTONSHIRE 1991

● Converted
○ Derelict
⊕ Preserved
〔〕 Remains

Barnack ⊕

⊕ Werrington

Easton-on-the-Hill ○

○ Castor

○ Tansor

● Cottingham

● Finedon

● Rushden

〔〕 Moulton

Barby ○   East Haddon 〔〕

● Northampton (Kingsthorpe)

Braunston ●

● Wootton

● Newnham

Hellidon ●

○ Blakesley

● Sulgrave   ○ Silverstone

N

Appendix 4

Name	Grid Ref.	Type	Condition	Remarks
ASTWELL	SP617450	?	Gone	
BADBY	SP554589	Post	Gone	
BARBY	SP541696	Tower	Store	
BARNACK*	TF073050	Post	Gone	
BARNACK*	TF069049	Tower	Preserved	
BLAKESLEY	SP622504	Tower	Store	'Quinbury End Mill'
BOZEAT	SP903585	Post	Gone	
BRAUNSTON	SP538662	Tower	House	
BRIGSTOCK	SP940858	Tower	Gone	
BYFIELD	SP515524	Post	Gone	
CASTOR*	TL129968	Tower	Shell	
CLIPSTON	SP702827	Post	Gone	
COTTINGHAM	SP849901	Tower	House	
EAST HADDON	SP656686	Tower	Remains	'Dexter's Mill'
EASTON-ON- THE HILL	TF008037	Tower	Shell	'Old Dexter's Mill'
EYE*	TF231030	Tower	Gone	Eight sails
EYE*	TF229036	Smock	Gone	'Eye Green Mill'
FINEDON	SP907724	Tower	House	'Exmill cottage'
GLINTON*	TF148056	Tower	Gone	
GREENS NORTON	SP667498	Tower	Gone	'Norton Mill'
HELLIDON	SP519578	Tower	House	
KETTERING	SP878787	Post	Gone	'Weekley Road Mill'
KINGS CLIFFE	TL004972	Tower	Gone	
LONG BUCKBY	SP646677	Post	Gone	
MOULTON	SP772662	Tower	Foundations	

*Soke of Peterborough

Name	Grid Ref.	Type	Condition	Remarks
NASEBY	SP686771†	Post	Gone	
NEW FLETTON*	TL192978	Tower	Gone	'Fletton Mill'
NEWNHAM	SP575609	Tower	Shell	
NORTHAMPTON	SP756639	Tower	House	'Kingsthorpe Mill'
NORTHAMPTON	SP762602	Tower	Gone	'Vigo Mill'
OLD	SP790743	Post	Gone	
OUNDLE	TL038887	Tower	Gone	'Glapthorne Road Mill'
PETER-BOROUGH*	TL202987	Post	Gone	'Fengate Mill'
PETER-BOROUGH*	TL188001	Tower	Gone	'Adams Mill, Millfield'
RAUNDS	SP995731	Tower	Gone	
RUSHDEN	SP956653	Smock	House	'Wymington Rd Mill'
SCALDWELL	SP759727	Post	Gone	
SILVERSTONE	SP674444	Tower	Shell	
STAVERTON	SP531612	Post	Gone	
SULGRAVE	SP553459	Tower	House	
SYRESHAM	SP629743	Post	Gone	
TANSOR	TL055910	Tower	Shell	
WELDON	SP928895	Post	Gone	'Hunt's Mill'
WERRINGTON*	TF165034	Tower	Store	
WESTON-ON-THE WELLAND	SP777906	Post	Gone	'Sutton Bassett Mill'
WOOTTON	SP759567	Tower	House	

†Approximate
*Soke of Peterborough

PIONEERS

*A youthful Donald Muggeridge with two eliptical springs from a pair of
spring sails — Sussex, 1935. [Photo: Donald W. Muggeridge]*

Donald Muggeridge (in cap) with 'Syd' Simmons during a field trip in Sussex in 1938. [Photo: Donald W. Muggeridge]

Donald Muggeridge with the late Rex Wailes (seated) in 1981.
Donald is one of the few surviving pioneers. His fieldwork and his skill with a camera,
during the decline of the use of windpower in the thirties, created for posterity a valuable
photographic record. He now lives in America, and the above photograph was taken in
his Californian home.
[Photo: Donald W. Muggeridge]

ENTHUSIASTS

Henry Wozniak inspecting a wire machine at Gedney Dyke, Lincolnshire. Henry, a meticulous researcher, gave the author invaluable help, and technical advice, in compiling this book. He and the author have together been on many field trips to various counties. [Photo: The author]

The author at Barnack. [Photo: The author]

Arthur C. Smith (conservationist, natural historian, author of a dozen windmill surveys in various counties, and writer of the foreword to this book) with his 'trusty steed' which carried him on many field trips. [Photo: Arthur C. Smith]

Nigel Moon, one of the few remaining windmillers in Britain, at Soham, Cambridgeshire. [Photo: The author]

Although situated outside Northamptonshire and the Soke of Peterborough, I could not resist adding to the collection this attractive study of Yaxley tower mill in Huntingdonshire. Built possibly in 1671, the mill was unique in having an 18 ft basement which included the piers of an earlier post mill. By 1933, when this picture was taken, the tailpole and four common sails had long gone, but the pulley wheel for steam power is evident. Sadly, this historic mill was demolished in 1935. [Photo: Peterborough Museum and Art Gallery]

Index